Harlequin Presents...

Other titles by

ANNE HAMPSON
IN HARLEQUIN PRESENTS

ANNE HAMPSON

waves of fire

Harlequin Books

TORONTO • LONDON • NEW YORK • AMSTERDAM • SYDNEY • WINNIPEG

Harlequin Presents edition published June 1973
ISBN 0-373-70510-7

Second printing June 1973
Third printing August 1973
Fourth printing November 1973
Fifth printing July 1974
Sixth printing August 1974
Seventh printing April 1976
Eighth printing June 1976
Ninth printing September 1976
Tenth printing February 1977

Original hardcover edition published in 1971
by Mills & Boon Limited

CHAPTER ONE

THE phone call was for Shani. Eagerly she took the receiver from her friend, but before she had time to speak Sister Glover entered the room and whispered,

'Matron wants to see you.'

'Now?'

'At once, yes.'

Shani spoke to Brian.

'Darling, I'll have to ring you back in a few minutes.'

'But, Shani—'

'Sorry. . . .' Replacing the receiver on its hook, Shani glanced in the mirror, smoothed her apron and went from the room, followed by Jenny, who had just come off duty.

'Poor Brian,' grinned Jenny, stopping by the door of her room.

'I promised to ring him back in a few minutes. He won't pine away in that time.' Shani smiled happily at her friend.

'Wedding bells soon?' asked Jenny, opening the door.

At that a slight frown touched Shani's brow. She said awkwardly,

'Not for a while, Jen.'

'You are going to marry him, though?'

'He hasn't asked me yet, but—' The smile reappeared. 'Of course I'm going to marry him,' finished Shani with confidence.

'Then why wait?' Jenny eyed her friend curiously, noting her fluctuating colour and the clear evidence of uncertainty in the movement of her hands. 'Is it that you can't bear the thought of having to leave here?'

'I must admit the idea dismays me,' confessed Shani, seizing on the second question as a means of avoiding the first. 'I shall certainly be sad when the time does come.' Through the window at the end of the corridor she could see the blue Mediterranean shimmering under a cloudless Cyprus sky.

The hospital stood on a high rise overlooking the lovely Bay of Loutras. Being the largest and most efficiently-run hospital in Cyprus, it was favoured by the British immigrants and consequently one or two English nurses had obtained posts there. Matron was also English, as were two of the doctors.

Matron glanced up and smiled as Shani entered the room in response to her 'Come in'.

'Ah, Sister, I thought you might already have gone over to the annexe.'

'I've been talking to one of the patients.' She gave a little grimace. 'Mrs. Forster.'

'She's still nervous about the coming operation.' Rising, Matron crossed the room to close one of the shutters; it was not yet half past eight, but the sun was becoming unbearably hot. 'However, she'll feel better on learning that you'll be there. I sent for you to tell you your request has been granted; you've been transferred to the theatre.'

Shani thanked her, endeavouring to hide her elation. Theatre work had always appealed to her and on coming to the Loutras Hospital two years ago her one ambition was to work with Mr. Rodgers, senior

6

consultant of the neuro-surgical unit. But to everyone's dismay Mr. Rodgers had now been forced into retirement owing to ill-health. A kindly, tolerant man, he was the most popular doctor in the hospital and it was generally accepted by those on the neuro-surgical ward that the new consultant could not possibly be as charming, whoever he might be.

'The new surgeon will be arriving tomorrow afternoon,' Matron went on to add. 'I know you're off duty then, but I want you to hold yourself ready to meet him. He's rather eccentric, I'm told, and quite likely to demand to see his staff immediately on his arrival.'

Eccentric? What would he be like to work with? Shani wondered, thinking regretfully of Mr. Rodgers' early retirement.

'I'll stay about,' she promised. 'What time will he be here?'

'His plane gets into Nicosia at two-thirty, so he should be here about an hour later.' Matron went on to discuss Mrs. Forster's coming operation, which the new surgeon would perform. 'From what I've heard about him Mr. Manou won't have much patience with her nervousness—'

'Manou?' The colour drained from Shani's face. 'Andreas Manou?'

'Do you know him?' Matron looked anxiously at her, for it was patently clear that Sister Reeves was badly shaken.

'I thought – thought the new surgeon's name was Manolis.'

'A mistake, obviously. Do you know him?' repeated Matron, her expression changing to one of curiosity.

'He used to work in a London hospital.' That inadequate statement only served to increase the older woman's puzzlement and Shani stammered, 'He w-was a colleague of – of my father.'

'I see. But that would be some years ago?' Matron still regarded her with that questioning look and Shani made an effort to regain her composure. She succeeded, outwardly, but the wild beating of her heart was something over which she had no control. 'How long has your father been dead?'

'Five years.' Was it so long ago that it had happened? How time did fly!

'Mr. Manou is still at the London hospital – or at least he was until yesterday. He is coming to us from there, and will be based here at Loutras for about a year.' Matron paused contemplatively and Shani feared she would be questioned further, but at that moment the telephone rang and all Matron said was, 'Don't forget, Sister, be ready to meet him.'

Ready to meet him. . . .

On reaching her room Shani felt so weak that she sank down on the bed. She had known, since realizing how she and Brian felt about one another, that she would have to contact Andreas – but never had she contemplated a meeting with him.

Refusing to dwell either on the coming ordeal or the one that had long since passed, she went downstairs and rang Brian back. He merely wanted to confirm their dinner date for that evening, and just twelve hours later they were dining by the sea, under a shelter of vines, their faces fanned by a breeze drifting across the warm dark waters of the Mediterranean. Above, a crescent moon hung over the sea, a silver arc in a sky lit by a million stars.

They ate mullet freshly-caught and garnished with crisp brown potatoes and salads, finishing off with figs newly-picked from the tree and sweet Turkish coffee. They danced to *bouzouki* music before, guiding Shani to the steps leading down to the beach, Brian put a possessive arm around her shoulders and rehearsed to himself the question Shani knew must come. The night was magical; the time would never be more right, and after walking in silence for a moment or two he whispered, his lips close to her ear, 'I have something to ask you, Shani. I'm sure you know what it is?'

This was what she had anticipated ... what she desired.

'I think so.' Her voice was shy and hesitant; a little laugh broke from Brian's lips and his arm tightened, bringing her close.

'I love you – love you! Darling, will you marry me?

Her eyes lifted. The breeze had tousled his hair. How attractive he was – and how everyone envied her! But her mind was disturbed as she struggled vainly for the right words. What sense was there in prevarication? Why search like this for a gentler way of imparting her news? Twisting from his embrace, she turned, her lovely eyes seeking escape from his by an intense concentration of the distant line of darkness where the sky met the sea.

'I'm already married,' she said without emotion, and in the silence that followed she began to wonder if he had missed her words, for they were no more than a whisper on the clear night air.

'What did you say?' Brian found his voice at last; it was high-pitched, yet oddly harsh.

9

'It's true. I– I've been married for five years.'

'Five years! But you're only twenty-three now—' Roughly she was brought round to face him. 'Married! What sort of nonsense is this!'

'Unfortunately it isn't nonsense. I was forced into it – blackmailed.' Shani saw again that dark pagan who, having seen her but once, became consumed by a desire that could not be suppressed. 'I left him.'

Another silence, broken only by the murmur of waves tossed gently on to the shore.

'I don't believe it,' declared Brian at last. 'Forced? Blackmailed? What are you talking about? You're lying!' But his tone had lost its vehemence; he knew better than to suspect Shani of lying. 'Oh, God, Shani, how could you lead me on like this? Why didn't you tell me before?' He released her and she moved away, flinching at the despair in his voice.

'It'll be all right, Brian,' she told him quickly. 'I can get an annulment. You see, I ran away before – before – I ran away before the marriage was consummated.'

The significance of this brought Brian from the stupor into which he had fallen. Hope rose, yet puzzlement was still there and for the moment he only asked accusingly,

'Why didn't you tell me? You've known for some weeks how I felt about you.'

'Not weeks,' she denied gently. 'It was a fortnight ago to be exact—'

'We've been going out together for three months,' he cut in wrathfully. 'Three months!'

'It was just the odd dinner date at first, if you remember? It was only at Sister Smallman's party that I realized you thought more about me than any of the others—' She stopped, flushing at her lack of tact. But until he began taking her out, Brian Davies, the handsome young R.A.F. officer stationed near Limassol, had been a notorious flirt. 'What I mean is,' she added hastily as he stiffened, 'it was only a couple of weeks ago that I began to think you were serious – that you would ask me to marry you. I decided then to write to Andreas, telling him I wanted an annulment.'

'Andreas?' he echoed, diverted. 'Isn't he English?' They were walking along the beach and automatically made for a low wall and sat down. 'He can't be Greek, surely?'

Shani's gaze wandered to the sea, but her only vision was of a slim dark giant, striding purposefully across the lawn, wrathful condemnation on his cruel and arrogant face.

'My husband,' she said, wondering at her composure, 'is Andreas Manou, the brain surgeon.'

'Andreas Manou? I've heard of him. He's performed several miracle operations. That's right, isn't it?'

She nodded.

'As I told you, Father was a doctor. Andreas worked in the same hospital.' She paused and added with the greatest difficulty, 'He's – Andreas is our new consultant at Loutras.'

An astounded silence followed. Brian seemed not only incapable of speech, but also incapable of comprehending this last piece of news. Shani tried to speak, to break the awful silence, but she could not, and at last Brian said, in rasping tones that made her wince,

'Coming here – your husband! God, what a coil!'

'Brian,' she pleaded, 'don't speak like this to me—'

'How do you expect me to speak!'

She frowned. It was sympathy she needed, and understanding. A tender word of reassurance and hope would have strengthened her, but all she received was the force of his anger and a glance that could only be described as baleful.

'Brian—' She stopped, her composure no longer supporting her as the present faded and memory returned, refusing to be thrust away. 'Perhaps I should tell you the whole.'

'I think you better had.' The hostile note increased her fears. Had she lost him? It was so odd that on meeting him her marriage had not seemed in the least important; there was no obstacle to a speedy annulment that she could see, and Brian would understand and wait patiently until she obtained it. But now ... now Shani was not at all sure. 'At least you owe me that,' he added through thin, compressed lips. 'I've been made a fool of, led on—'

'No – oh, no! Don't say that. This episode in my life was my own affair. The reason for my leaving England was so that I could start afresh. This was natural, and right from the first I retained my own name – from the moment of leaving him, I mean. In fact, I have never once used his name.' She looked pleadingly at him, but his face was turned away and all she saw was the hard profile and sulky set of his mouth. 'You can't blame me for not telling you until I was sure.'

'Well, seeing that you are sure, let's have the truth. I love you and want to marry you, so don't keep anything back, if you please!'

Not at all the approach she would have expected. No sign of compassion, no immediate willingness to listen to the whole story before displaying angry accusation, no loyal declaration that she must be blameless. Shani was afraid. If she were to lose Brian now. . . .

'It all began really when Mummy died. You see, Father took to drink. . . .' The quiet dispassionate manner in which her story was related amazed Shani, but then she seemed not to be telling the story at all, but to be re-living it as she sat there, on the low wall by the waterfront, under a magical Cyprus sky.

He had descended upon them one fine sunny day in September, the dark and sinister Greek with fire in his eyes and black fury in his heart. Little did Shani know, as she watched his approach, of the upheaval Andreas Manou was going to cause in her life.

They were in the garden having tea, two ordinary people living their quiet uneventful lives. Dr. Reeves, stout and greying, had a slight stoop and walked with a limp. This was a result of a war injury when a piece of metal lodged close to his spine. It could not be removed and one day it would prove fatal; that day could be soon, or a long time off. He had lost his wife a year previously and to Shani's dismay had become addicted to drink.

'You shouldn't, darling, being a doctor,' she had repeatedly warned, but even though he knew of her fears he could not control the habit. For his wife had been so lovely, and he so devoted to her. Just like Shani she had pale gold hair and wide blue eyes. To the last her features had retained the delicate lines and entrancing contours that had captured his heart on their very first meeting. Shani took after her mother in every way, even possessing the same build, perfectly proportioned if, in Shani's case, not perfectly developed, as she was only just eighteen years old. Her cornflower blue eyes had already upset many hearts, her smile sent them racing. None of the other trainee nurses was more unsophisticatedly beautiful than Shani, none possessed a nature so in keeping with the captivating loveliness of the veneer.

She was the first to see the man; he came striding across the lawn, having been to the front of the house where, presumably, he had left his car. She frowned a little, for he reminded her of some sleek and dangerous animal, with claws unsheathed, ready to tear its victim to shreds.

'Andreas ... how come you to be here?' Rising, Dr. Reeves proffered a hand; seconds later he let it fall to his side, his face paling as he saw his visitor's expression. 'Is anything wrong?'

Involuntarily Shani looked up at the sky; it was as if a dark cloud had obscured the sun, so changed was the atmosphere by the presence of this man, and Shani felt an icy shiver pass slowly along her spine.

'I'll speak to you privately.' The Greek never gave a glance to Shani and even as the introductions would have been made he snapped out, 'Immediately!'

The two men went towards the house; Shani followed them with her eyes. The Greek was clearly under some great strain, his face being dark and drawn, making more pronounced the lines running from nose to jaw, lines that lent an evil aspect to a face that already carried a manifestation of cruelty in that the eyes were as hard as tempered steel, and the lips thin and tightly compressed. Andreas Manou, the eminent brain surgeon whom her father had several times mentioned, their both being employed at the same hospital. Andreas had recently performed a miracle operation and the newspapers had carried headlines about it. The patient was still in hospital, making a most satisfactory recovery.

What could a man like Andreas Manou want with her father? Suddenly his visit became an event of vital importance, for it must be a most serious matter that could not wait until the morning, or even be discussed on the telephone. For some inexplicable reason Shani's heart raced and that icy shiver crept along her spine again. Unable to rest, she left her tea and went into the house, entering by a different door and standing unashamedly outside the room in which Andreas and her father talked.

'You were drunk! I've warned you, over and over again—'

'No – no, Andreas, you shall not say I was drunk! You'll never be able to prove it!'

'Would you have prescribed that drug had you been sober?'

'I – I—' As her father's voice broke Shani had to keep a firm grip on herself, her one desire being to go in to him, but this was not the time to do so. 'Is he ... dead? After your wonderful operation?'

The voice of the Greek came to Shani, soft and menacing like the low drawn-out snarl that precedes the attack.

'If he had died, Reeves, you would have killed him. What right had you to prescribe a drug for my patient?'

'I was attending to someone else and the man couldn't sleep. You weren't there and I felt I couldn't disturb you, so I gave him something.'

'My orders were that I be called were I needed. Fortunately I woke and decided to get up and take a look at him. You'd gone by this time – too drunk to remain, I suppose!'

'No!' Dr. Reeves shouted the word, startling his daughter so that she actually jumped. 'I wasn't drunk. You can't prove it.'

'I can – and have – proved that the wrong drug was administered on your instructions, and had I not decided to get up when I did the patient would have died – *died*, after all my work!' He paused and it seemed to Shani that his anger was mingled with conceit. Andreas Manou was said to possess a certain arrogance and conceit, but because of his incredible skill these were excused. 'How will you answer the charge?'

Charge! Shani's heart turned right over, leaving her shaking visibly.

'The nurse – it could have been her fault—'

'You coward!' cut in the Greek with a snarl. 'You cowardly wretch. But have no doubts, my friend, you're the one who'll pay for that error, and pay dear. You're not fit to have men's lives in your hands.'

Shani's trembling increased. That her father had made a terrible mistake was evident and the consequences could have been disastrous. No wonder Mr. Manou was furious. As he said, the man could have died— She checked her thoughts, for they terrified her.

The men were still arguing – or rather, one accused while the other denied. And as she listened Shani suspected her father of crying and tears started to her own eyes; his suffering had been so great, and often he would sit and reminisce, while Shani patiently listened, even though she knew she was a phantom audience, as her father was really quite alone.

'The first time I saw her I wanted her, she was so lovely, so very lovely. And it was not only on the surface – no, your mother was the sweetest-natured woman that ever lived.' Although he mentioned Shani in a roundabout way he still was not with her, or she with him. He was alone with the woman he loved. But one day he did become aware of his daughter's presence; he looked straight at her and said, 'It will be the same with you, Shani. The man will come one wonderful day; he'll see you, and know that you are his.'

Shani made no comment. She did not believe that love at first sight could happen very often. Moreover, in her opinion it would be a miracle if both were of the same mind. And it was no use the man loving on sight unless the woman could return that love.

'I don't want to marry for a long while yet,' she had said at length, giving him an affectionate smile. 'My career's only just beginning.'

'Yes, I know, and it's the one I would have you choose, but don't become so dedicated as to let the wonderful state of marriage pass you by.'

'The way I feel at present I want to spend many years at nursing. Marriage has no appeal for me.'

Her father had frowned at first and then smiled faintly, saying that when the right man came along, and fell in love with her on sight, she would be powerless to resist him.

Back to the present Shani was brought with a jerk as

she realized the voices had stopped and that the Greek was walking towards the door. Stepping back into the other room, she sped through it with the intention of returning to her chair in the garden, but as she reached the outside door she literally fell into the arms of the tall stranger as he strode furiously from the house.

'Oh!' breathed Shani, wincing at the pain of his grip on her arms. 'I'm sorry. . . .' The collision had left her panting slightly and as she tilted her head right back in order to look at him her breath caressed his face, soft and warm and clean. Her lovely lips were parted and her startled eyes, staring into his, were the colour of an eastern sky at noon. From an incredible height he regarded her, his dark eyes strangely softened by wonderment and disbelief.

'You must be Shani?'

'Yes,' she murmured, wondering why he did not release her. 'Yes, I'm Shani.'

'Shani. . . .' The name rolled on his tongue, enriched by the hint of an accent. 'How very charming.' Whether he meant the name or the girl she never knew, because the hardness returned to his face as her father appeared from the room behind him.

'Andreas, for God's sake, is there nothing I can do or say to make you change your mind? The drink – Shani will tell you, I never touched it until my wife died and I felt so utterly shattered. . . .' He tailed off as he took in the scene before him. The Greek's attention was once more with the girl he held in his arms. 'Shani, what are you doing?'

Flushing hotly, she gave a little twist to release herself as the pressure on her arms was relaxed.

'I bumped into Mr. Manou.'

Allowing that explanation to pass without comment, her father renewed his pleading with Andreas.

'Surely you're human? You won't report me—?'

'Human. . . .' Andreas kept his eyes fixed on Shani's face as if he would never take them off it, and there was the most odd inflection in his voice as he murmured, almost to himself, 'Yes, I'm human.'

Misunderstanding that rather obscure remark, Shani added her pleas to those of her father.

'I overheard much of what you said to Daddy,' she admitted, her cheeks colouring adorably. 'And what he said just now is quite true; he never drank until a year ago, when Mummy died.' She still stood very close to Andreas and as she raised imploring eyes to his she had no idea how desirable she appeared to him, in this attitude of supplication. 'Please keep silent, Mr. Manou. He won't ever drink again. I know he won't.'

'I swear it!' said Dr. Reeves fervently. 'Give me a chance, I beg of you. You'll not denounce me – I somehow can't believe you will.'

Andreas was still occupied with the vision before him and despite her growing discomfiture at the intensity of his gaze Shani determinedly examined his face, surprised by the fact that the first impression of cruelty was fading somewhat. Did he really intend exposing her father? More likely, she concluded, it was his intention to frighten him, and as he had plainly succeeded Shani was on the point of feeling grateful when the dark Greek confounded her by saying,

'You just asked me what you could do, Reeves. You can give me your daughter.'

A bird twittered in the solitary tree at the end of the

garden, and that was the only sound as the three looked from one to another. Overhead the clouds had thickened, blotting out the sun completely. Shani glanced up, frowning. The sudden darkness seemed like an omen of perils to come.

'I don't think I understand you.' The doctor spoke at last, passing his tongue over lips that had become white and parched.

'I'm offering for your daughter,' explained the Greek in calm unruffled tones. 'There's nothing unusual in that.'

'Andreas,' said the doctor after a pause, 'it might be the practice in your country for a man to choose a girl and offer for her, but you are not in Greece now.'

'I'm a Greek, nevertheless,' smiled Andreas, glancing in his direction, 'and naturally I conduct my affairs in accordance with the customs to which I am used. I'll take Shani from you, and you have my promise that she'll have care and – consideration.'

The older man shook his head dazedly, unable to admit that the Greek could possibly be serious. As for Shani herself, through the mist of her bewilderment she was wondering about the slight hesitation; Andreas had most certainly been going to say something quite different when, with what appeared to be a hasty check, he had altered it to 'consideration'. Presently she shrugged. What he had been about to say interested her no more than what he actually had said.

'In this country we don't give our girls away,' her father was saying. 'Shani will one day fall in love, and her husband will be a man of her own choice. Her future's entirely in her own hands.'

'And your future's in mine.' So softly he spoke, but

again Shani was reminded of an animal, panther-like, ready to spring. Her father went white as the full significance of his colleague's words became clear to him.

'I can't believe you're serious – when you offer for Shani, I mean,' he said feebly, spreading his hands. Catching his expression, noting the haggard lines that all at once added years to his age, Shani slowly and tremblingly accepted the fact that her father knew this formidable Greek had never been more serious in his life. Andrea's next words proved her conclusion to be correct.

'I don't waste my time saying things I don't mean. I desire to marry your daughter and I'm requesting you to give her to me.' No answer from the doctor and Andreas added quietly, yet with a sinister threat in his words, 'Your daughter in return for my silence.'

Having been an impassive onlooker in the drama in which she should be playing the chief role, Shani spoke at last, her chin in the air.

'You've just reminded us you're a Greek, and that you conduct your affairs according to the customs of your own country, but as Father has reminded *you*, you're not in Greece now. This is England, and your customs appear rather ridiculous to a westerner.' A slight was not intended, but unfortunately Shani bungled her phrasing and the Greek's straight black brows knitted together ominously as he said, in those familiar soft and menacing tones,

'May I say your arrogance appears rather ridiculous to me, under the circumstances. Your father is in a most precarious position, his future career and good name being entirely in my hands, as I've already said. According to how I decide to act he will retain his position and the respect of his patients and friends, or he'll retire into ignominious seclusion.'

'His work is his life,' she cried, her flash of arrogance bitterly regretted. 'Oh, you can't denounce him!' Unconsciously she twisted her hands in a distracted sort of way, for there was no doubt at all that they were completely in this man's power. If only he had not seen her. . . . But he had seen her, and desired her – just as he would had she been a woman of the East – and the hold he had over her father was now a tool to be used in blackmail. 'You can't do this to us! Father's learned his lesson without any serious damage being done, so please let it pass. He won't ever touch drink again—'

'Never,' declared the doctor. 'I'll make a solemn promise about that.' His voice was unsteady and Shani thought it must touch some soft chord in this man's make-up, but she reckoned without the primitive desire she had awakened in him, a desire that she soon realized was enveloping him so entirely that any chivalry he did possess was for the present submerged.

'I've stated my terms.' He spoke to Dr. Reeves, ignoring Shani altogether, just as he would have done had she been a Greek girl for whom he had offered. In his country the prospective bridegroom – or in some cases his parents – and the girl's father would arrange the union, with the girl herself meekly accepting what was planned for her. 'Your daughter – or exposure, take your choice. Perhaps you'll let me have your decision tomorrow.' He was about to walk away when Dr. Reeves' voice arrested him.

'I can give you my decision now,' he said brokenly. 'Go ahead and report me—'

'Father, no!' White to the lips, Shani moved closer to him, placing a hand on his arm in an effort to comfort him. 'You can't decide without considering the consequences.'

'I have considered them.'

'Wait until tomorrow, darling. You can't think clearly at present.' She would not look at the man responsible for all this misery, but she knew that for the first time in her life dark hatred burned in her eyes.

'You have my decision,' her father said stiffly, and waved a hand towards the gate in a gesture of dismissal. Andreas stood where he was, watching Shani's back.

'I'll give you until tomorrow, all the same,' he said in a voice whose confidence could not possibly be missed. 'I shall not change my mind.'

'No?' Strong brown hands were quite unexpectedly on Shani's shoulders, and Andreas turned her gently round to face him. Deeply he looked into her eyes and although he could not possibly miss the hatred there he saw something else as well, something which he had apparently expected to find, for he said, with a smile of triumph which only served to increase Shani's hatred for him. 'I wonder, Reeves, I wonder . . .?'

The wedding was a fashionable affair, as Andreas had many friends both Greek and English. Shani had friends too and on seeing Andreas for the first time at the wedding they all made whispered exclamations.

'Where did she meet him? He's terrific!'

'Through her father, I expect. The great Andreas Manou – lucky thing!'

'He's so handsome and distinguished.'

'And famous. What more could any girl want?'

'They say he's never had the slightest interest in women.'

'But you must admit Shani is *something*! I'll bet he fell in love the moment he set eyes on her!'

'Could have – seeing how the wedding's been so rushed. Shani dined with us three weeks ago and could talk of nothing else but her career. I'm sure she hadn't even met him then.'

'Hush . . . here they come. Have you ever seen a more striking couple? And that dress – they say it's been flown over from Greece – was made, every stitch by hand, for Andreas's great-great-grandmother.'

'All that lace – made by hand?'

'So the papers said. The Greek women spend their lives sewing and embroidering.'

'That necklace, all diamonds! A family heirloom, probably.'

'She looks like an angel. I'll bet every man in church is envying her husband!'

But as Shani walked towards them, her hand resting stiffly on her bridegroom's arm, her lips tight and her eyes unmoving, the whispered comments took a different turn.

'Shani . . . she doesn't look happy!'

'Her eyes – how sad. . .'

'Not a smile for anyone; that's not like Shani.'

'She must be happy. It's nerves.'

'I think you're right. It must be nerves.'

She was very pale, but a most beautiful bride for all that. Later, at the reception, she stood with her husband and wondered if any bride had ever felt as desolate as she. Her father's eyes met hers and in them also dwelt the deepest misery. He had wanted to take the consequences of his folly, rather than sacrifice her, but Shani's had been the decision. Her father's sufferings over the loss of his wife were still great, but he loved his work and as it kept him almost fully occupied he had little time left in which to brood: Were he to be exposed and brought into disgrace, a disgrace that must inevitably result in a life of forced idleness, then that life would not be worth living. Unwilling to see this happen, Shani had made her decision and would not waver from it. She would marry Andreas, but she would also make him rue the day he ever put that ultimatum to her father.

This she told herself over and over again without any clear idea of how she would pay Andreas back, and as she glanced up at him, standing there by her side as they shook hands with the guests, she felt her heart was dead within her. She would never be a match for him, would never commit any act of reprisal without bringing down some punishment on her head. He was of the East, where a woman, having the status of a mere possession, submitted without question to her husband's will. And hadn't Andreas said, when making his 'offer' for her, that he would conduct his affairs according to the customs of his own country?

For a long while she stood there by the dressing-table musing over the events of the past two weeks. The tragic death of her father just as he was leaving the wedding reception. His death had given Shani a respite made more bitter by the fact that she had prayed for some miracle that would save her from this formidable Greek to whom she was married by consent and yet assuredly by force.

Andreas had been kind, this she grudgingly had to own. And certainly everything had been taken out of her hands. But the loss, coming when it did, not only upset her nerves, but was also the cause of an increased resentment against her husband, for had he not hurried her, insisting on the wedding taking place when he desired it should do so, she would never have married him at all.

Naturally the honeymoon was postponed as Shani was stricken with grief, but after a fortnight she had begun to sense an impatience in her husband, an urgency which she took for desire and which, to her disgust, he did not seem able to control.

'We'll go away for a few days,' he had said, and even though she guessed at the futility of pleading she had asked for more time. Firmly he had refused, impervious to her tears. 'You don't think it now, Shani, but you'll feel better for the change.'

'Perhaps I would, if I weren't married,' she cried, wringing her hands. 'Can't you wait a little while longer?'

He remained adamant and there came to her the idea that had persistently intruded into her mind for the past week. But it would be too dishonest, she had kept telling herself. Voluntarily she had entered into marriage, knowingly she had accepted the fact of Andreas's being different from her both in temperament and appearance; vaguely she had become resigned to occupying an inferior position to that which would have been her lot had she married an Englishman. No, she could not cheat – she must not.

And so when he had remained firm she had meekly

packed her things and accompanied him to Folkestone, where he had suggested they spend their honeymoon. He had chosen the best hotel, booked the most luxurious suite.

Her musings were interrupted by the appearance of her husband, and it was only on seeing him in dressing-gown and pyjamas that she realized how long she had been standing there. His brows lifted at her appearance; he slowly advanced towards her and she did not resist when he took hold of her hands. But she was pale and afraid. What sort of man was this whom she had married? Dark and sinister, a foreigner in whose blood ran the pagan traits of his idol-worshipping forebears, he would crush and subjugate her until she had no will of her own, no personality, no life other than that of a slave, a possession to be used, indifferently laid aside, and used again as this man's passions and desires dictated. Shani knew the colour had left her face, she also knew – or thought she knew – that Andreas was impatient, that soon she would encounter a fury that would make her present fear seem no more than a small fluttering of trepidation.

'Are you intending to stay up all night?' he inquired with a sort of gentle humour. She did not reply, but her pallid cheeks fused with colour and he flicked at one of them caressingly. 'Don't be afraid of me, Shani. I'll not hurt you.'

Hurt? Hadn't he hurt her already? – just about as much as he could do? He had ruined her life, utterly.

'If – if you will give me time . . . ?' Her lovely eyes pleaded, her hands were outstretched in a gesture of entreaty. 'I'm still shocked by Father's death, and you . . . you're still a stranger to me.' No answer came to her pleadings and she thought she detected a certain harshness and inflexibility in his eyes that convinced her she wasted her time. And yet she tried again. 'Tomorrow night, Andreas, *please* let it be tomorrow night.'

'Tomorrow?' He considered this, but as his expression was inscrutable she could not read his thoughts. After a while she felt her whole body sag as he firmly shook his head.

'Tonight, my dear, it must be tonight.' A strange hint of fatality in his voice caused her to lift her head sharply. 'If you stay with me tonight you'll stay with me for ever.'

She frowned. What an odd thing to say— The blood rushed to her face as his meaning – or what she concluded to be his meaning – was made clear. However, for the present she did not comment on it, merely saying, with an unconscious glance at the door,

'You're afraid I'll leave you, now that Father has gone?'

He swallowed, profoundly stirred in some indefinable way, for there was a movement in his jaw as if a strong emotion were being held relentlessly in check.

'You could leave me, Shani, and I would not want that.'

Her lovely head went high in the air.

'You desired me on sight, didn't you? I don't now believe for one minute you'd have exposed Father. You used your knowledge to get me, a woman you had set eyes on and instantly desired. But now you're to live with this fear, which is really a punishment—'

'I have never known fear in my life, Shani,' he intervened in quiet and gentle tones. 'I said I would not want you to leave me, but fear did not prompt those words.'

'In Greece, I suppose, a wife would never dare leave her husband?'

'In Greece a woman rarely even thinks of leaving her husband.'

'She resigns herself to subjection, to the supreme mastery of her husband?'

'Her husband is the master, yes,' he admitted. 'But – subjection? I don't think I understand you?'

'Mastery and subjection – what difference is there?'

The question brought a slight frown to his eyes. She felt he could have explained better in his own language.

'There is a difference, Shani, for I dislike intensely the word subjection, while mastery does not trouble me at all.'

'It's your intention to master me?'

He frowned but said firmly,

'I shall guide you and advise; I shall not let you make mistakes that could bring unhappiness or hurt to either of us.'

'How very subtle!' The sneer in her voice made him start in surprise; it was so out of character with the gentle nature he had come to know during the short period of their acquaintanceship. 'What you're really telling me is that you'll restrict and order, that you'll curb my will. And also you're warning me not to look at another man – ever.'

The last sentence had an effect on him that terrified her; his face took on an evil, primitive expression as his lips were drawn back and his eyes, naturally dark as are those of most Greek men, seemed to become almost black as the embers of jealousy smouldered in their depths. Shani stepped back, but his hand caught at her wrist and she was drawn to him, feeling the heat of his body and the mad throbbing of his heart. Never had she known such fear, never had she thought to have a husband possessed of emotions as unbridled as this savage from the East.

'Another man!' he snarled, his dark face almost touching hers. 'Yes, my lovely Shani, that's exactly what I did mean! Look at another man and I'll kill you – understand? You're mine, my wife, for always. And if you ever forget that it will be to your cost!' His lips closed on hers, cruel and demanding, as if he would force reciprocation from her despite her undisguised aversion for him. She did not struggle, and presently her gentleness, and the tears produced by fear, affected him as strongly as had her words about another man. His hands became softly caressing and she thought of him as a surgeon, using those hands in the service of his fellows, saving life. His lips too were gentle and when he held her from him at last she whispered hopefully,

'Tomorrow night?' But again he refused her request.

'If you stay with me tonight you'll never leave me – never, I'm very sure of that,' he said again, and this time she did comment on it, her eyes revealing all the contempt she felt for him as she retorted,

'That is the only way you can be sure of keeping me, isn't it? You forced me into marriage and now you've to resort to this method in order to make sure I'll stay with you. What satisfaction will you derive from it? I'll never really be yours.'

Her husband's eyes were faintly puzzled; it did not dawn on Shani that she could have misunderstood the meaning of his words.

'What exactly are you saying?' he inquired softly.

Shani thought of someone she knew who had married a Greek. The Greeks talk quite openly of 'making a baby' and before she had stopped to think Shani had repeated to Andreas what this Greek husband had said to his wife on the day of their marriage. But Shani soon tailed off, shrinking away, this time from the icy contempt that had replaced the savage fury in his eyes.

'I do not speak broken English,' he informed her coldly. 'Nor do I consider myself so inadequate in other ways that I must of necessity resort to using this method you suggest in order to keep my wife at my side.'

Shani lowered her head under the rebuke. It was a most odd circumstance that although this man was so blame-worthy it was she herself who experienced a feeling of guilt.

'That's what you meant,' she murmured at length, merely for something to say because the long accusing silence only served to increase her inexplicable feeling of blame.

Andreas shrugged impatiently.

'Believe that if you must; but later, I think you'll change your mind.'

Change her mind about what? He spoke in riddles. Had he not just said that if she stayed tonight she would stay for ever, so what else could he mean?

She fell silent and after a while he asked her again if she were going to remain there all night. There seemed to be no possible means of escape and, taking up the nightgown and negligée that lay on the bed, she turned towards the bathroom, half expecting Andreas to pass some sarcastic remark about her action, but he said nothing, and on her return he was in his own room. The dividing door had swung to and although it was not latched it was almost closed. Shani's eyes kindled with an odd light as all her good resolutions became submerged by the fear that engulfed her at the thought of the ordeal to come. She couldn't go through with it. . . . Her glance moved from the separating door to that leading to the corridor. Had she time to fling on her clothes again? Where could she go? Aunt Lucy! Spinster, man-hater, she had refused to attend the wedding, merely expressing disgust at the idea of her brother's allowing Shani to get married, especially to a doctor, and one seventeen years her senior. Aunt Lucy would never contact Andreas, never insist on Shani's returning to him. Yes . . . she would be quite safe with Aunt Lucy. And Andreas would never find her, hidden away as she would be right up there in Nottinghamshire. Lucky she had never mentioned her old aunt, very lucky indeed. . . .

CHAPTER TWO

They met in Matron's room, husband and wife facing one another after five years. As she made the introductions Matron said casually,

'Sister Reeves tells me that you were once a colleague of her father,' and although Andreas's eyes flickered he gave no other sign that he was affected by the fact that Shani had given Matron to understand they were acquaintances, and nothing more.

'Sister Reeves. . . .' An unmistakeable emphasis on the name; a strong yet slender hand extended impersonally; eyes that bored into her without the merest hint of recognition despite what Matron had just said. His perfect composure and air of superiority set Shani at an immediate disadvantage and in spite of her efforts to preserve her own cool front she felt her colour deepen. A world of unreality closed in upon her. This man, so tall and lean and, to her astonishment, indescribably handsome, was shaking hands with her in exactly the way he would have shaken hands with Nurse Weston or Sister Louzides. No surprise or accusation, no fury or hate looking back at her as she met and held his gaze for a brief space before lowering her head. Had he known she was here, had he expected this encounter and been fully prepared for it he could not have evinced less emotion. 'Tell me, Sister, how long have you been here, at Loutras?'

'Two years.' The taking of a post abroad had been for the sole purpose of putting as great a distance as possible between her husband and herself.

He became thoughtful, as if calculating mentally. Shani gained the impression that he was impatient with himself about something.

'Two years in Cyprus, eh?' he said musingly, a small sigh following his words. Shani frowned. Was it possible that he had been looking for her? But hadn't she told him, in the scribbled note she left, that he need not try to find her as she had no intention of ever living with him? – nor even using his name?

And yet . . . This total lack of surprise was unnatural even in a man so notoriously unemotional as the celebrated Andreas Manou.

He and Matron were conversing and as she stood apart, free to dwell on the idea that was slowly gaining strength, what had begun as a tingling of uneasiness reached the proportions of real consternation before Shani was eventually overcome by an access of dark foreboding that would not be quelled. If he *had* been looking for her it could only mean one thing; his desire had not waned in all these years. And if his desire were still as strong as ever then how would he react to the suggestion of an annulment?

Supposing he would not free her? Supposing she could not marry Brian, after all? As if to add to her misgivings a sudden flash of memory brought back that frightening scene when Andreas had sworn to kill her should she ever look at another man. Not that he had meant it literally, of course, but Shani knew his threat was not to be taken lightly.

She marvelled now at her sublime unconcern regarding the matter of an annulment. But then she had assumed that Andreas would welcome his freedom, believing the time must come when he would want a wife in his home, and children. It now occurred to her that had he ever contemplated an annulment he would have done something about it a long while ago.

She must see him at the first opportunity, she decided, unwilling to dwell on the scene with Brian should the interview with Andreas not produce the desired result.

However, she could not see him at once. She had a week's leave and was going away that very evening to visit some English friends who were on holiday in Famagusta. In three days' time Jenny would be on leave and she would join Shani and her friends in the lovely beach-side bungalow they had rented.

'Lydia Murray's getting along fine with our new surgeon,' was the information Shani received on meeting her friend at the bus station. 'He's terribly abrupt with everyone except her – none of us envy you, incidentally. He's darned attractive, but I should imagine he'll be hell to work with.' A small pause, and then, 'There's a rumour he's been married – and divorced.'

'Lydia Murray,' said Shani quickly, ignoring her friend's last statement. 'They're friendly, already?'

'Mr. Manou appears to be friendly with her – or perhaps I should say he's rather less abrupt with her than with anyone else at the hospital,' amended Jenny with a grimace.

'He's naturally abrupt,' submitted Shani, still in the same abstracted way, as Jenny looked sharply at her, 'I noticed this during the short time I was with him. He was even abrupt with Matron.'

'I'd hate to be in your shoes, having to work with

him all the time. It's so awful when you can't answer back.'

That brought an involuntary smile to Shani's lips. What would Jenny think were she to say, 'But I can answer him back. I'm his wife'?

But she was not his wife in any way at all. A ceremony into which she was forced, promises made when her mind was blanked out with misery and despair, a first night that had ended abruptly when in panic she had fled from him, complete absence of communication between them since. How could she be married to him?

Jenny made some further remark about Lydia, and Shani resolutely dismissed Andreas from her mind and concentrated on what her friend was saying.

'I thought Lydia was working? Has she left?'

'She works part-time only, in some office. But as you know she's helping Dr. Gordon with his book and so she's in the hospital quite often. Elli says she met Mr. Manou in the dining-room and was immediately all over him. They've had lunch together today, and Elli says she saw Lydia going to Mr. Manou's house the evening before last.'

Would they become more than friends? wondered Shani with a surge of optimism. Would Andreas fall in love with Lydia and want to marry her?

'Do they go out at night, do you think?' she queried eagerly, and Jenny's fair brows lifted.

'They haven't had much time. Even Lydia is not as fast a worker as that!'

'No. . . .' Shani blushed as her friend glanced oddly at her. 'Mr. Manou has been with us only four days. But,' she added absently, 'Lydia's very attractive, and he might fall in love with her straight away.' Wishful thinking? Certainly. Nevertheless, Lydia Murray was more than ordinarily attractive, in a cool and sophisticated sort of way. She and Andreas would in fact make a most distinguished-looking couple.

'If they did make a hit of it many people at Loutras would be pleased. Lydia's becoming a nuisance.'

'She hasn't any real authority. Why does she think she can come into the hospital and give orders?'

'For no other reason than that her father's one of the subscribers to the hospital funds. She's bored, and this gives her something to do.' Having reached a *taverna* they automatically stopped for a drink. The tables were outside, shaded from the sun's glare and heat by vines growing over a pergola. They sat down and gave their order.

'If she got married,' said Jenny, 'and had a baby right away, it would please everyone. She'd have no time to potter about the hospital the way she does, issuing orders.'

'I don't expect she'd have to look after her own baby,' commented Shani, seeing Lydia in her immaculate attire, with never a hair out of place. 'She'll marry someone who can afford to pay a nanny.'

'Mr. Manou can afford to pay a nanny, I expect. Let's hope something happens in that quarter.'

Shani laughed.

'We've had hopes like this before,' she reminded her friend. 'Do you remember Dr. Greyson?'

'Wasn't handsome enough for her – nor rich enough. She's mercenary, that one.'

Four days later Shani knocked on Andreas's door. The hospital was not the place for the discussion of so private a matter, but she must speak to Andreas before meeting Brian on Friday. Brian was coming up for the weekend and Shani hoped to be able to assure him that the annulment would go through without delay. To her surprise the door was opened by Lydia, who stood there, waiting for Shani to speak.

'I want to see Mr. Manou. . . .' Glancing past Lydia, Shani observed that the room was empty. 'I want to speak to him privately, but I see he isn't—'

'Privately?' Arrogant eyes flicked Shani from head to foot. 'He isn't here.'

'I was about to say that,' returned Shani with unaccustomed tartness. 'Will he be long?' Why was Lydia in his room? she wondered, though not with any particular interest.

'I can't say how long he'll be, but in any case he won't want to be disturbed. Can I give him a message?'

'Tell him I'll call at his house this evening. I'll be there at seven o'clock.'

'His house!' The exclamation had the effect of making Shani bristle, and her little chin lifted aggressively.

'Yes, Miss Murray, I shall call at his house.'

The dark eyes kindled.

'He won't be in at seven; he's dining at my home.'

'Dining at seven?' Shani could only stare for a second or two. People did not dine at seven here. Nine it was, or even later.

'He won't be in at seven,' repeated Lydia, and closed the door. Shani walked away, biting her lip. The interview with her husband would not be pleasant and her one desire was to get it over and done with as soon as possible.

The following day she and Andreas met in the theatre. On becoming acquainted with the man who was to perform the operation Mrs. Forster had completely lost her fear, and it was Shani whose nerves were fluttering when Andreas walked unsmilingly in and bade her a curt,

'Good morning, Sister.'

'Good morning – Mr. Manou,' she murmured in response.

Andreas ignored everyone else, having already seen the anaesthetist a short while earlier. Shani watched as he put on his gown and cap, assisted by the junior theatre nurse. His eyes met Shani's as he put on his gloves, then they moved to the prone figure of the patient and finally to the anaesthetist sitting by her side.

As the first incision was made Shani wondered what he felt like at these times when he held a precious life in those long and slender hands. One slip of a millimetre. . . .

Her own hand shook as she passed him the required instrument; she heard a smothered intake of his breath and felt he was aware of – and impatient with – her slight nervousness. Was he despising her for it? Most probably, she decided, and realized with amazement that the idea actually hurt.

The heat was intense and he was perspiring heavily. He would lose weight, then have to make it up, for it was imperative that a surgeon keep perfectly fit. At a gesture from him the junior nurse mopped his brow; his eyes met Shani's and in that fleeting moment before he looked away again Shani felt herself moved by some unfathomable, elusive quiver of emotion.

At last it was over, after several hours, and Mrs. Forster was wheeled out of the theatre. Andreas looked tired but by no means exhausted. Shani on the other hand could have fallen asleep where she stood. She took off her mask; Andreas looked critically at her, his eyes unsmiling, his jaw flexed.

'Better come and have some tea,' he said abruptly as they left the theatre together. 'We'll have it in my room.'

Now, she thought, as she sat back in the chair he had pulled forward for her, was the time to broach the subject of the annulment, but she could not frame the words.

'It's been a strain for you,' observed Andreas, examining her face closely. 'The first time is, naturally, hard on the nerves.'

'You knew it was my first time?'

'Matron had told me of your transfer, but I would have known in any case. You gave yourself away a dozen times.'

She flushed and because she was so tired her lips moved tremulously. He smiled faintly and said there was nothing to cry about. In fact, she had surprised him by her apparent coolness and efficiency.

'I'm not crying,' she retorted, her eyes flashing indignantly. 'I'm just a little tired, that's all.'

The tea came and he poured it out, handing hers over to her. They drank in silence, with Shani several times making an attempt to bring up the matter of the annulment but failing because somehow the time was not right, after all. They were both too tired, with their minds filled with the recent drama. She would call at his house tomorrow afternoon.

But on knocking on the door she wondered if she had chosen the wrong time. However, her third knock was answered, but to her dismay she saw that Andreas had been sleeping. He wore a dressing-gown and his hair was ruffled.

'I'm sorry,' she began, 'I'll come back some other time. I'm so sorry I've disturbed you—'

'What is it, Shani?'

'I wanted to talk to you.' She hesitated uncertainly for a moment and then, 'If you can spare me a little time – I mean what I have to say won't take a moment.'

'It's a personal matter?' He eyed her searchingly. She saw his eyes harden.

'Yes, it is a personal matter.'

Andreas opened the door wider and stood aside for Shani to enter.

'In here.' He gestured with his hand and she entered the sitting-room. 'Sit down, Shani. Can I get you a drink?'

'No, thank you.' Her heart raced madly, just as it had on that night when he had taken her into his arms and forced his kisses upon her, kisses that had so terrified her she had conceived and carried out the idea of escape. She sat down on one of the chairs, endeavouring to relax but not succeeding to any great extent.

'What is it you have to say to me?' Andreas perched himself on the arm of the chair opposite to her, his hands thrust into the pockets of his dressing-gown.

'It's about our marriage,' she began, amazed that her voice could remain so clear and steady. 'I want an

41

annulment.'

A profound silence followed that last brief sentence, with Andreas sitting there, waiting in an attitude of inquiry as if expecting to hear more. Shani swallowed hard and added something about its not being difficult to procure an annulment in a case such as theirs. The silence continued, and now it was Shani who waited. What an unreal situation, she thought. Here they were, husband and wife who were strangers, she requesting her freedom so that she could marry another man, and Andreas just sitting there, apparently unmoved. Unmoved . . . ? She caught her breath. A paleness had crept under his skin, but it was the light of tempered steel in his eyes that set every nerve in her body quivering.

'It should not be difficult, you say?' His tones were soft, expressionless . . . and yet inflexible. 'Now what gave you that idea, I wonder?'

A chill swept over Shani. She recalled her earlier misgivings and the impression she had gained that Andreas had been searching for her. Highly skilled, and having achieved fame at a comparatively early age, he had left one of London's largest hospitals to come to Loutras, a circumstance that had astonished not only the entire staff at Loutras, but the staff of the London hospital too.

'We've never lived together.' She daren't mention Brian, not yet, but she knew Andreas must surely inquire as to the reason for her request. 'I thought you might be finding it irksome – being tied, I mean.'

'Had I found it irksome I'd have done something about regaining my freedom before now.' Moving to the cabinet, he opened it and poured himself a drink.

42

'We're married, Shani,' he stated inexorably. 'And we stay that way.'

'You'd stay married to a woman who doesn't want you?' She shook her head in a gesture of disbelief. 'We can't go on like this for the rest of our lives!' Panic seized her as she thought of Brian. On hearing her story he had become mollified, telling her of his plans for their future. He would be stationed on the island for another year and if the annulment could be effected soon they would be able to have a wonderfully long honeymoon on this paradise isle before returning to England and facing reality in the form of buying and fixing up a house – and starting a family. This was what Shani wanted, and this was what she meant to have. 'If you're going to be obstinate,' she went on angrily, 'then I'll engage a lawyer and let him see to having the marriage annulled!'

'Indeed?' Andreas took a drink and put the glass down on the table. 'How little importance the English attach to the marriage tie,' he said with the hint of a sneer.

'You appear to have forgotten that I was forced into the union with you.'

Andreas's straight black brows lifted a fraction.

'Forced? My dear Shani, can you honestly say that?'

'Don't let's split hairs, Andreas,' she pleaded. 'I really had no choice, had I?'

An odd expression settled on his dark face and Shani was reminded of her doubts at the time. Was it his intention to expose her father as he had threatened? – or had he merely meant to frighten him, to ensure there would be no more drinking when on duty? She shrugged.

What did it matter? The past was dead; it was her future with which she was wholly concerned.

'You had the choice. No person can force another into marriage, especially in your country. You agreed to marry me; it was with your father's consent. Under such circumstances I fail to see how you can obtain an annulment.'

She flung out her hands.

'You ... you're tied too!' A mistake, both the all-revealing gesture with her hands and the emphasis on the last word.

'Why,' asked Andreas softly, 'are you so anxious to obtain your freedom?'

She swallowed hard and managed to say,

'I've met someone else. I – we want to marry. ...' The rest died on her lips and what little colour she had receded from her cheeks. She could not take her eyes off Andreas, for he had sloughed the mask and she saw the heathen slowly emerging from the deceptive cover of refinement.

'Marry! You want to marry someone else! You *are* married,' he snarled, his eyes smouldering with jealousy. 'You're my wife! My wife for ever, I told you that a long while ago. I also warned you you'd forget it to your cost! – so don't ever dare forget it!'

White to the lips, Shani rose unsteadily from her chair, making a sideways movement in order to avoid coming too close to this man who could be a cultured doctor one moment and a savage pagan the next.

'I'd b-better be g-going,' she faltered, taking a backward step in the direction of the door. 'I'm sorry now that I came—' She got no further; her wrist was gripped and she could not move. A dark face was close,

44

and fear leapt into her eyes.

Inhuman, capable of any torture, this Greek whose desire for her had shattered the peace which both she and her father had enjoyed until that fatal day he had entered her life. 'Let me go!' Useless to struggle and yet her natural instincts were brought into action. 'You've no right—'

'Right? I've a right to do what I like with you! I've the rights of a husband, and for a start I'll exert them by—' He did not finish but drew her into an embrace so painful that she felt herself imprisoned in bands of steel. His lips possessed hers, merciless and, to her terrified imagination, burning with desire. Shani's struggles ceased and she stood passive in his arms, praying this onslaught would spend itself in kisses only, yet at the same time acutely conscious of the unbridled intensity of his passion, and of the danger which threatened. For a start. . . . No mistaking the significance of that, and Shani renewed her struggles. How imprudent to come here, putting herself in his power. But she had not thought his desire would be as strong as ever, not after a span of five long years.

At last he held her away, and looked deeply into her eyes.

'You haven't changed, my little wife. You're more beautiful, I think, and even more desirable.' He was once more the cultured gentleman, a husband exhibiting all the tenderness and gentle persuasion any wife could have desired. 'Shani, my little girl, can't we try? You'll never know how I wanted you . . . how I looked and looked, never thinking you'd be abroad. My dear, can't we live together and be happy? Why did you leave me?' For a man of such strength his voice was

45

oddly broken, and so were his phrases, as if he just said what came into his mind at one particular moment. 'If you'd stayed ... I told you, dear, do you remember? I told you that if you would stay with me one night you'd stay for ever. Live with me, Shani; I know we can be happy.'

So her suspicions were correct; he had been searching for her.

She quivered under the touch that had become so gentle, and an emotion she could not analyse crept over her. Yet all her revulsion was present, her disgust at his primitive desire when, on first setting eyes on her, he had resolved to make her his, no matter how he crushed her in the process, or marred a life that was only just beginning.

'Live with you?' she cried, her mouth and body still hurt and bruised. 'How can you suggest such a thing? Besides, you seem to have forgotten that I'm in love with someone else.' A mistake; too late she realized it. The fatal reference to another man fanned the flame that had momentarily died down and Shani knew again the uncontrolled intensity of his passion. And then she was thrust from him, to go staggering back against the couch.

'In love!' he snarled, white-lipped. 'Where is this man? Does he know you are already married?' He pointed to the couch behind her. 'Sit down and we'll talk about it. I must meet this man who is under the illusion he can rob me of my wife!'

Shani remained standing by the couch, valiantly trying to regain a little of her composure. But she was badly shaken and her face was white. It seemed unbelievable that because of a certain fatal attraction she

46

had for this dark foreigner she must be made to suffer in this way.

'Brian knows I'm married,' she quivered, her lovely eyes meeting those of her husband despite the fear she had of him, and of what she would read in his expression. 'I promised him I'd get an annulment.' Despair engulfed her. That she would eventually obtain her freedom she felt sure, but would Brian wait? He had a reputation for being attracted by a pretty face and had indulged in numerous trifling affairs before finally discovering he could settle down with Shani. Reflecting on his anger on discovering she was married, Shani felt she could never acquaint him with the news that the annulment would be delayed.

'Sit down.' Andreas again indicated the couch and this time the softly-spoken order was prudently obeyed. 'So you promised him you'd get an annulment, did you? That was rather rash, don't you think?' He sat down on the chair, so calm and controlled that it seemed impossible the scene just ended had ever taken place. 'What gave you the idea I'd agree to a break-up of our marriage?'

'Andreas,' she whispered on a little pleading note, 'we've never really been married.'

His eyes darkened and she caught her breath. What was he thinking? she wondered fearfully.

'We've never made love,' he returned with the typical Greek outspokenness which had the effect of bringing the colour rushing back into her cheeks. 'You didn't even give our marriage a trial—'

'I was afraid of you,' she uttered fiercely and in tones meant to remind him of his impatience at that time, and of his injustice towards her father. 'Also I was only eighteen, Andreas, you seem to have forgotten that.'

'So you were, Shani. Eighteen. . . .' He spoke so gently that she stared at him, bewildered. 'I realized very soon that I hadn't allowed for your youth, your timidity or your natural fear of me – a stranger. And so I didn't search for you right away. I waited – allowing you to grow up while you finished your training. And then I did begin looking for you—' He broke off, and turned away from her to refill his glass. 'By this time you must have gone abroad. It was quite by chance I discovered your whereabouts; a patient was flown from here to the London hospital; he talked about Loutras, naturally, and mentioned Sister Reeves . . . Sister Shani Reeves. . . .' His voice dropped and could scarcely be heard. Shani said, diverted for the moment,

'You obviously came here for the sole purpose of asking me to live with you, but there was no need to leave London, no need to come here to work. You could simply have paid me a visit.' He stared into his glass, twisting it between his fingers.

'I required time,' he returned cryptically. 'What I had in mind couldn't be done quickly.' Shani frowned, and would have questioned him, but he prevented this by adding, 'However, that's unimportant now, because the circumstances aren't what I expected.'

What did he mean – the circumstances were not what he expected? Was it that he had believed she would still be heartfree? And if so, what were these intentions of his that could not be carried out quickly?

'I don't understand?'

'It doesn't matter. As I said, it's now unimportant.'

He held her gaze, and a regretful smile dispelled every line of harshness from his face. 'You've just reminded me that at the time of our marriage you were young – and afraid of me. But now, my dear, you're older, and you know what it's all about. We're irrevocably bound together, and so it's better that we try, Shani, for we've a long way to go and the road can be lonely.' The nature of his words and the manner in which he phrased them took Shani by surprise. The softness of his tones, also, and the way he looked at her, were in such contrast to his former vicious demonstration that she could only sit there, regarding him in wordless astonishment. 'Think about what I've said,' he advised. 'Think carefully, my dear, keeping in mind that our marriage is permanent whatever your decision.' Glancing at the clock, he added apologetically, 'You'll have to excuse me if I ask you to leave. I've a friend coming over from Athens today and I must get dressed. I'm meeting him at the airport.' He looked steadily into her eyes. 'Think about my proposal, Shani. Consider it seriously.'

She stood up, discarding his offer, and concentrating instead on how she was to break the news to Brian.

CHAPTER THREE

BRIAN was furious. He raved and stormed and finally gave way to bitter frustration. Listening to him, and noting his ever-changing expression, Shani experienced a severe sense of shock. Disappointment she naturally would have understood; a small show of pained accusation she felt she could have forgiven, but this. . . . Without doubt, she decided, three months was no time at all in which to get to know a man with Brian's particular temperament.

For a short while she listened without comment, but after the first miserable, dejected moments she was compelled to retaliate. Not only must she suffer at Andreas's hands, but she must also endure Brian's bitter tirade and say nothing! Gentle as she was, and loath to quarrel with anyone, Shani felt she had had quite enough of men for the time being. Nothing that had angered either man could be placed at her door and, turning on Brian, she informed him in no uncertain terms that she was utterly without blame in this matter.

'Without blame?' he rasped, eyes burning. 'You say that, after leading me on the way you have!'

'I didn't lead you on! How was I to know you weren't flirting with me as you always flirted with the others? As soon as I guessed you were serious with me I decided to write to Andreas. Our friendship developed in the end more rapidly than I expected and you proposed before I had time to contact him.' She stopped, a little ache in her heart. Nothing would ever heal this breach between Brian and herself, she felt sure. 'If you had any thought for my feelings you'd be sympathizing with me, and – and suggesting ways and means of assisting me to regain my freedom.' She brushed a hand across her eyes, but Brian was too enveloped in self-pity even to notice.

'It doesn't look as if you'll ever regain your freedom. He wants you and I can't see him giving up possession in order that some other man can take it,' he told her crudely, and Shani instantly stood up.

'Take me home,' she requested in a suffocated voice. 'I never want to see you again.'

'Eat your dinner and don't be melodramatic!'

Her eyes sparkled and her little chin lifted.

'If you don't take me home I'll call a taxi.'

She meant it, and Brian's knife and fork dropped with a clatter to his plate. Flushing slightly under the stares of nearby diners, he rose to his feet.

'Good night,' he almost shouted twenty minutes later on dropping Shani at the entrance to the hospital. '*Mrs. Manou!*' And he drove away in a cloud of dust.

Mrs. Manou. ... Never before had anyone called her that – unless of course one of the guests had teasingly done so after the wedding.

How strange that she had not once considered herself as married. Tied, yes, but not irrevocably. The marriage she had always regarded as a sort of tangle in which she had become enmeshed, but one from whose cords she could, with a little manipulation, quite easily escape. How wrong her supposition had proved to be! Perhaps, she reflected unhappily as she mounted the stairs to her room, she should have kept in mind that inflexible streak possessed by her husband. Hadn't she pleaded in vain on another occasion? – begged him to give her a little more time?

Mrs Manou. That Brian should say that to her, and with such bitter emphasis. She would never forgive him, never!

She sat down on the bed, stared at the pillow, and for a brief moment was tempted to give way to tears. But no, she would not! If this were the depth of Brian's love she could do very well without it. And as for Andreas – she would hate him for the rest of her life! The least he could do was make amends by granting her the freedom she so desperately desired.

Her condemnation of both men remained for a while, but inevitably her anger against Brian began gradually to fade and as the days passed she found herself waiting expectantly for a phone call. Surely he would ring; this couldn't be the end. Hadn't he chosen her in preference to any of the girls he knew? – loved her sufficiently to want her for his wife? No, this could not be the end, she emphatically told herself. But when the days lengthened into weeks and still there was silence Shani began to despair of ever seeing Brian again. However, she did see him, a month after informing him of the probable delay over obtaining the annulment.

She and Jenny had decided to have a meal out and they dined in the Turkish quarter of Nicosia. One couple only were sitting in the restaurant . . . Brian and an old flame of his, whom he had thrown over soon after meeting Shani. She gave Shani a rather condescending glance not unmixed with triumph; Brian's glance was startled. He flushed and became absorbed with the contents of his plate. Jenny's eyes hardened; she steered her friend to a table at the other end of the room – as far away as possible from the couple seated in the intimate, dimly-lit alcove.

'The beast!' Jenny was unable to remain silent as she glowered at Brian. 'You're better off without him. He's the island's biggest flirt!'

'Yes, I'm better off without him.' Shani looked at her friend, fully aware of Jenny's puzzlement. Shani had merely said that she and Brian had quarrelled and it was only natural that Jenny should be curious as to the reason for the quarrel. This Shani could not disclose, and to her relief Jenny had not pressed her with questions.

Brian and Debbie were laughing. So swift had been his recovery! How could strong and sincere love fade so quickly? Strong and sincere love. . . . An abrupt, involuntary switch of her thoughts found her recalling what Andreas had said about searching for her. Desire, it would appear, was far stronger than Brian's so-called love. But what of her own feelings for Brian? Hurt she undoubtedly was, seeing him sitting there with another girl. Her mouth trembled, but she held her head proudly erect, and throughout the meal she kept up an animated conversation with her friend, assuming a careless pose.

But how her heart ached! From the nagging pain of jealousy emerged a sudden appreciation of her husband's feelings. His jealousy stemmed of course from the mere desire for possession, which was far removed from the spiritual love which Shani felt for Brian. That she should be feeling much more desolate than this did not at present strike her; all she knew was that the dull ache of jealousy settling upon her excluded all but the vision of a future unbearably lonely and bleak.

Her glance strayed to the alcove; Brian was still laughing, yet now Shani sensed his gaiety was forced. On his departure half an hour later he nodded casually, but Shani somehow formed the impression that his indifference afforded him scant satisfaction.

And the following day he did ring. Full of apologies, he asked to see her.

'Let me take you out? Do you still have all day Tuesday off?' She murmured 'yes' and he continued, 'We'll take a trip to Kyrenia, get in some swimming and then dine out in the evening.' She made no comment and he urged on a note of contrition, 'Please, Shani. . . . I was a fool to go off at the deep end like that. Forgive me. Come out and let's talk about this damnable affair without rancour on either side.'

She had not harboured rancour – at least not at first – she could have reminded him, but she refrained. She had longed for a reconciliation and here it was offered. No sense in antagonizing Brian again. She accepted his invitation and he came for her in his car. He had three days' leave and had arranged to stay with friends in a small village not far from Loutras.

The drive began in silence, but after the inevitable period of awkwardness Brian began to talk, determined to make amends for his unsympathetic behaviour on their last meeting. Shani soon forgave him . . . but where was the thrill of making up? – the excitement of regaining his love? Something seemed to be lacking – something noticed by Shani but evidently not by Brian, for he was in the best of spirits.

Later, after their swim, they lay on the sands. Shani regarded him broodingly, wondering at the void within her. The pardon was of her own volition, the fullness of which she could readily bestow, but memory . . . ? Memory was a dangerous and destructive thing. And as she lay there, her slender body darker by far than the golden sands around her, Shani owned with dismay and bitter reluctance that she would never be able to forget Brian's condemnation and lack of understanding.

What exactly did she feel for him? she asked herself. If one forgave there must be allied with that forgiveness the desire – and the ability – to forget, otherwise a bitter rankling remained. Perfection in her relationship with the man she would marry was essential to Shani, whether her husband was to be Brian or some other man she would meet in the future. Some other man! Was it only a month since Brian had occupied all her thoughts? – had been the only one for her? Impatiently she cast off these troublesome meditations and gave herself up to the pleasures immediately offered. Diving into the water, she found it warm and calm, gleaming turquoise close to the shore, while in the far distance it changed to a lighter blue, cut by the serpentine channels of purest crystal flecked with silver.

She came up to Brian and they floated side by side, talking. Then Shani took possession of the li-lo and lay staring up at the sky, cloudless and shimmering and flushed with translucent gold. On leaving the water they had the beach entirely to themselves.

'The sea's fabulous here.' Brian dried his body, spread the towel on the sands and lay down on it. Shani did the same. Moments passed; the only sounds were the murmur of waves touching the shore and the shriek of a bird circling over the raised beach that formed the bare and rocky backshore.

'Can we talk now?' Brian's eyes were dark and contrite. 'I'm sorry, truly I am. And the other evening,' he added hastily, a hint of colour rising, 'I didn't enjoy it one scrap. I'd much rather have been with you.'

There was a whole month when he could have been with her— Deliberately Shani checked her thoughts. If she and Brian were to pick up the threads there could be no recriminations; she must be prepared to forget, make a supreme effort to overcome her difficulty in doing so.

'I haven't done anything about the annulment.' Scooped sand trickled through her long brown fingers. She watched it pensively.

'My fault,' owned Brian, reaching for her hand. 'You'd naturally feel there was no immediate hurry.' He gave her hand an affectionate squeeze. Shani could not respond. Why should her thoughts be with her husband? Why should she choose this time to dwell on his admission that he had 'searched and searched'? 'You'll set the ball rolling now?'

'If you want me to,' she answered vaguely, a sudden frown darkening her brow.

'Certainly I want you to.' He lay on his side, resting on one elbow, regarding her with tenderness. Her doubts began to dissolve and she felt a little happier. Brian wanted her, and that was all that mattered.

'I've another day off on Monday. I'll go into Nicosia and engage a lawyer.'

'Good girl! As you said, there shouldn't be any

difficulty.'

'There'll be a delay, owing to my being abroad.'

'How long?' and when she shook her head, 'No, of course you can't possibly say.'

'It'll take a few months, I expect,' she ventured, and received immediate reassurance from his smile.

'I can wait, although it won't be easy. However, we'll be seeing each other in the meantime.'

She moved closer to him and his arm went round her waist.

'We'll have a longer engagement, that's all,' she murmured, lifting her face.

He kissed her tenderly.

'I was a fool, Shani. Forgive me, darling.'

She had forgiven him, but she conveyed the message only with her eyes, for all at once speech had become difficult. A certain strain had entered into her relationship with Brian and Shani was greatly troubled by it.

Meanwhile in the hospital Andreas treated her with the familiar impersonal coolness; she was no different from any other of the nurses. Lydia, on the other hand, was – as Jenny crudely put it – making headway by leaps and bounds.

'She'll get him,' she declared emphatically one day as she and Shani were standing at her room window watching Lydia on her way to the villa in which Andreas lived. The door opened on the instant of her knocking and Jenny declared he had been eagerly awaiting his visitor.

'I wonder what she does in there?' Shani said musingly, and Jenny's brows lifted. 'I mean,' she added hastily, 'Lydia could be doing some clerical work for Mr. Manou, just as she did for Dr. Schofield.'

'She could,' Jenny agreed laughingly. 'But it's most unlikely. She's made a hit, that's easy to see. Whether or not he's serious it's difficult to say, but she certainly is.'

Shrugging, Shani made no comment. It would simplify matters if Andreas were to fall in love, he would then be as eager as she to obtain an annulment.

'Mr. Manou's in a foul mood.' Jenny came up to her friend just before the operation was due to begin. 'What's wrong with him?'

'I think he's fairly certain, before he even starts, that the young man is going to be a vegetable.' The little Cypriot nurse spoke before Shani had time to do so. 'I heard him talking to Matron about it, and he seemed very depressed. The young man has a wife and two children, as you know.' She shook her head sadly. 'No wonder he's in this furious mood. All doctors hate motor-cycles.'

'Naturally,' said Jenny on a grim, half angry note. 'Look at the work they'd be saved if motor-cycles had never been invented.' She threw a deprecating glance at her friend. 'I don't envy you. If he's in this mood before he starts he's going to be far from pleasant to work with.'

And Jenny had not exaggerated. On entering the theatre Andreas bade Shani a curt 'Good morning, Sister' without even sparing her a glance. He scrubbed up, his face harsh and taut. As Crystalla, the junior theatre nurse, helped him into his gown she ventured to smile at him – and received a scowl for her trouble. His obvious ill-humour only served to increase the tenseness of the atmosphere and as Shani caught the glance of

58

the anaesthetist she knew that he too was wondering what Andreas would be like after several hours in the theatre.

His orders were snapped out; he glowered at Shani for no reason at all and when, her nerves all keyed up, she made the mistake of handing him the wrong instrument he flung it across the floor.

Hours went by, hours fraught with tension; on Andreas's brow great beads of perspiration would appear, to be mopped away by Crystalla who was standing by his side.

Suddenly Shani's attention was arrested by the gravity on the anaesthetist's face as he checked the patient's heartbeats. He spoke urgently to Andreas; speed was vital if a collapse were to be avoided. A soft oath was the surgeon's immediate response and Shani realized that on beginning the operation Andreas had cherished the hope that a miracle could be performed. He was now having to admit that the patient's brain would never function properly, that he would be a liability to his wife and family for the rest of his days.

At last it was all over and Shani watched his expression. It held a mixture of anger and frustration. Defeat was something Andreas Manou could not bear to face.

The following day he looked through Shani as they passed in the corridor. The slight was unintentional, she knew, but the fact that Lydia witnessed it had a strangely irritating effect on Shani. Later, they met again in the corridor; Shani hurried past, but this time Andreas called to her.

'Sister – one moment.'

She turned, her eyes flickering to the far end of the

corridor. Matron was there, talking to Dr. Charalambedes. Shani had to extend respect to her superior.

'Yes, sir?'

'I want you at my house this evening. I've something to discuss with you.' His tones were soft but penetrating as he added, 'Be there at seven – prompt!'

Shani presented herself at five minutes to seven. The door was ajar and he bade her enter. Her heart raced, and her legs were not acting normally either, she suddenly discovered on entering the sitting-room. Had he received a letter from her lawyer? It would appear so – and it was just her luck that it should come at this time, when he was so depressed about the operation.

'Sit down.' He waved a hand, indicating a chair, and she sank into it. 'What's all this about an annulment?' he demanded, just as if it had never previously been discussed.

'You've heard from my lawyer?'

'I've asked you a question,' he said, an edge to his voice. Shani was distinctly put out by his attitude. She stammered awkwardly,

'I've already t-told you I want my freedom.'

'And I told you,' he pronounced with emphasis, 'that we stay married.' He stood with his back to the window, a dark figure with unmoving features. 'Obviously you haven't given any thought to my suggestion that we try, that we live together?'

She stared at him astounded.

'We're strangers,' she exclaimed. 'How can you expect me to live with you?'

'We're husband and wife, Shani.' A voice quite soft, and yet Shani sensed a quality of ruthlessness about this formidable foreigner that set her nerves tingling. He reminded her again, after all these years, of an animal about to spring – an insidious calculating animal waiting to forestall any self-defensive move. 'You and I are tied irrevocably, I told you that. We're bound, Shani, until one of us dies.'

Involuntarily she shook her head, as if the idea hurt. Her throat felt dry and she coughed to clear it.

'Can I get you a drink?' he asked, surprising her by his perception.

'Yes, please— Sherry,' she added as he was about to ask what she preferred.

A deep sense of unreality swept over her. This man's forceful personality, his quiet strength ... his determination to remain married to her when he must know that was absolutely impossible. All these threw her into a state where reasoning became an effort. Away from Andreas everything appeared uncomplicated; in his presence she saw only difficulties ahead. Why had he entered her life? Why had he ever set eyes on her, desiring her from the very first moment? But having seen her, why hadn't his ardour cooled in all these years? She looked into his face. Lean and dark, it was a proud face, and strong; handsome too in a primitive sort of way. Within her an emotion quickened, stirring her senses in a manner that thrilled even while it terrified.

Shocked by this new sensation, she averted her head, wondering what strange powers this dark unfathomable Greek possessed. Her glass was handed to her; the drink gave her heart, infused her with the courage to inquire once again if he had heard from her lawyer.

'I received a letter this afternoon. That's why you're here.' He drank deeply, then stood staring into the glass for a moment. 'You're wasting both your time and your money.' He paused, waiting for her to look up. 'We're married, and the sooner you become resigned to that the better.'

Her pulse fluttered. Andreas was so confident, so cool about it all. And yet what could he do?

'The — the lawyer said an annulment would be simple.' Her eyes, so large and expressive, were faintly pleading. 'I want my freedom, Andreas. You forced me into this marriage and you can't possibly expect me to stay with you — not without love.' Frowning as those last words were uttered, she wondered at the haggard lines appearing on her husband's face. The result of yesterday's frustration? But no, this was not frustration. More like anguish and a deeply penetrating hurt — which was of course ridiculous. Andreas Manou would be the last man to suffer anguish and hurt.

'What did you tell this lawyer of yours?' he asked, ignoring her words.

'Everything; I had to.'

'What is everything?'

'I said you made me marry you by threatening Father with exposure — and of course I said we had never lived together. That's my strength as regards getting an annulment.'

'Is it now? How little you know, my dear. Did you tell this man who I was?' he added before she could speak.

'I couldn't do anything else.' She took another drink. 'I'm sorry to do this, but I must have my freedom.' Andreas was a famous surgeon; in every way his reputation was high. Naturally he would not wish anything of an unsavoury nature to touch his name. But he should have thought of that when he forced her into a union which had no possible chance of success.

'And your lawyer told you an annulment would be simple.' His eyes were cold as steel, his jaw hard and flexed. She searched his face as he stood there, sunk into the depths of preoccupation, his slim lithe body framed in the window. Was he facing defeat? Certainly he was not accepting it. That tingling sensation returned as Shani's gaze moved to rest on the fingers holding his glass. Muscular and sensitive, they gripped the stem so firmly that she actually steeled herself for the breakage. It did not come. Placing the glass on the table, Andreas advanced towards her chair and stood there, his height overpowering. She looked up, moved by some irresistible force to meet that penetrating gaze, and as they stared at one another Shani knew again that profound, all-consuming emotion and the colour swept into her cheeks. Admiration flickered for an instant, but the harshness remained. No, not a sign of defeat in those dark and wide-set eyes, just firmness and resolution, and a confidence that troubled her greatly. 'You're obviously ignorant of the fact that lawyers here are reputed to know little of the English laws?' She did not answer and he went on, 'This man you've engaged doesn't know what he's talking about.'

'Certainly he knows!' she cried, with more defiance than conviction.

'You're aware of the ease with which the Cypriots can dissolve a marriage, I suppose?'

She frowned. Where was this leading?

'They obtain a divorce by mutual consent.'

'On paying the church a considerable amount of money,' he supplemented with a faint smile. 'However, what I was really trying to point out is that this lawyer of yours apparently believes an annulment will be just as simple. Did you tell him we were married in England?'

Her spirits began to sink, even while she obstinately refused to admit that Andreas had the power to keep her bound to him.

'He knows we were married in England, yes.'

'And yet he believes he can obtain an annulment for you.' Andreas shook his head. 'Only I can annul the marriage – you are not in a position to do so, whatever you, or this lawyer, might think to the contrary.'

'You?' She stared at him. 'But I'm the injured party. I was forced into marriage – blackmailed!'

'Don't talk rubbish! You married me willingly. As for your being the injured party, I must correct you there. I'm the injured party— No, wait until I've finished, please. I've offered you a home and you've refused to live with me. In the eyes of the law I'm the one with the grievance; consequently it is only I who can annul the marriage.' She put her glass on the table and sat back, her hands clasped, staring into space. Was this true? The uneasiness that had gradually crept over her was all-enveloping now. Was she really tied to this man for life? She lifted her eyes, silently pleading, but all he said was, 'I know you've given me your answer regarding our future, but is that your final word?'

'Certainly it's my final word. I'll never live with you – besides, you seem to have overlooked the fact that

I'm. . . . ' Her voice trailed off into silence as she noted his swiftly-changing expression.

'Yes,' he prompted softly. 'You're . . . ?'

Fear threatened to block her throat and she spoke swiftly, before her courage failed her.

'I'm in love with someone else, you know that.' A tense silence followed and when eventually she managed to look up Shani knew that had she glanced up sooner she would have seen something far different from the mild stare she now encountered. 'I want to marry him, Andreas, and if you have any honour at all you'll not stand in the way of my obtaining an annulment.'

'I've just said you can't annul the marriage. I've also said I must see this man who believes he can steal my wife from me. Who is he?'

'Brian – he's at the base.'

'An Englishman, eh?'

'It's only natural that I should want to marry a man of my own country.' She stood up, taking her handbag from the table. 'There isn't anything for us to discuss,' she told him quietly. 'The lawyer warned me not to be alone with you.'

'You must not be alone with your husband?' Again his manner was different from what she would have expected. 'What else did he say?' The quiet voice, the total lack of emotion – these should by rights have alarmed her far more than one of his violent demonstrations; instead, they had the effect of lulling her into a realm of safety where she found the courage to answer him in a way she would never previously have dared.

'He said you don't have a leg to stand on – and I

have confidence in his verdict, in spite of what you say!'

Just a movement in his throat . . . and a shrug of his shoulders before, turning, Andreas opened the door and stood aside, allowing her to pass through into the hall. The front door was open wide and round the patio lights flew dozens of giant moths. From the distance came the muted sound of waves brushing the shore. Turning to fasten the gate behind her, Shani saw that Andreas had entered the house and the front door was now closed. About to move on she found her eyes irresistibly drawn to the lighted window of the sitting room . . . and to the shadow on the wall. Frowning, she swallowed something hurtful in her throat. Andreas was sitting down . . . and his head was sunk in his hands.

CHAPTER FOUR

WHAT was this uncertainty assailing her, this tantalizing confusion of mind? She desired nothing more than to be free of Andreas. ... Most certainly she wanted to be free of him!

A week had passed since her last visit to her husband's house, a week in which she had fought to regain her clarity of vision. Brian was away, having been posted to England for a month, much to his disgust, but for herself, Shani felt a surge of relief at his going. By the time he returned she must surely have emerged from this bewildering cloud of uncertainty. But with each succeeding day her confusion increased, and at last she was forced to admit that the reason stemmed from the fact that Andreas intruded into her thoughts far more than was good for her peace of mind. The strange thing was that with these intrusions came the gradual recognition of herself as a married woman. Until a few months ago her marriage had been an unreal state which time would dissolve, but now she was coming to accept that state, and on one occasion she had actually taken her wedding ring from its box and looked at it, fascinated – and afraid to try it on. Mrs. Manou. ...

The lawyer had not done anything more. These matters took time, he had said when Shani last rang him, but he went on to assure her that he had the proceedings well in hand and she had nothing at all to worry about.

On hearing of the lawyer's optimism Brian had insisted on a premature celebration and had taken Shani to the Hilton. During dinner she had made several attempts to tell him of the summons to her husband's villa, but could not. So Brian had gone to England sublimely ignorant of Andreas's assertion that he alone had the power to annul the marriage.

'He's quite resigned by this time, I suppose?' Brian had said gloatingly as he sat with Shani in the car for a while before bidding her good night. 'It's not much use his being anything else, seeing that the lawyer's so optimistic.'

Avoiding a direct answer, Shani said,

'He could be mistaken – the lawyer, I mean. Perhaps he thinks it'll be easy as it would be here. As you know, in Cyprus even divorce is simple. The couple merely have to tell the priest they want the marriage dissolved and that's it. They're both free.'

'Pity it's not like that in England,' returned Brian, missing her point but bringing a heavy frown to her brow. So he was of the opinion that divorce should be easy. . . . 'Is he resigned?' repeated Brian when she did not speak.

A small hesitation. She was suddenly reluctant to discuss her husband in this way.

'He seems a little resigned, and yet—'

'A little!' sharply. 'What do you mean?'

'I must be frank; Andreas doesn't want to release me.'

'How stupid!' Brian frowned suddenly. 'But you acted as if he was resigned.'

The reluctance to discuss Andreas remained. In fact, Shani had an almost irrepressible urge to tell Brian to mind his own business, but soon admitted that this was most illogical of her and went on to explain that while on the one hand Andreas appeared to be resigned, on the other hand he had several times become so engrossed in thought that he might easily have been plotting something.

'You're being fanciful,' declared Brian. 'What could he be plotting?'

'There's nothing. It's as you say, I'm being fanciful.'

'Well, whether he's resigned or not he'll have to release you. The matter's entirely out of his hands.'

How little he knew, thought Shani, wishing she had had the courage to tell him the truth, tell him of Andreas's firm assertion that she had no grounds whatsoever for obtaining an annulment of the marriage.

A week after Brian's departure the staff were having a farewell party for one of the Greek nurses who was getting married the following Sunday. All the doctors were there, and those of the nurses who could be spared. Both Shani and Jenny were free to attend. Popular with everyone, not only because of her unusual beauty, but also because of her deep sense of honour and compassion, Shani came in for rather more than her fair share of attention from the doctors, and several times as she caught her husband's gaze fixed upon her she saw a glint of steel in his eyes. Lydia hovered confidently round him and now and then there would be whispers about them.

'Friends only,' asserted Dr. Charalambedes, his mouth close to Shani's ear. 'He'll not marry her, if that's what she's expecting.'

This struck Shani as amusing and she laughed, a tinkling laugh which once again afforded her attention from Andreas. He was handsome, she owned, meeting his gaze, and that feeling of unrest became so strong within her that she moved away from the small crowd around her and stood by herself, looking from the patio across the sea to the mountains of Turkey, hazed in heat and yet capped with snow.

Her mind was in a turmoil. Why should she suddenly resent Lydia's possessive attitude towards Andreas? – for she did resent it, even though she had laughed at Dr. Charalambedes' remark. She thought of Brian, gone a week now and not in the least missed. Shani had pangs of guilt about that, especially as she was now quite unable to picture a future as his wife.

'Are you not drinking?' The voice, low and vibrant, was yet tender somehow and Shani turned, soft colour rising in her cheeks.

'I left it on the table.'

Andreas fetched it for her and she took the glass from him, a shyness creeping over her as she looked up into his face.

'Thank you.' Mechanically she sipped the wine, conscious of Lydia's dark eyes regarding her. 'We're going to miss Androula.' Prosaic words, born of confusion.

'She's efficient, I agree.' Andreas paused, cool and self-possessed, and then, 'Shall we sit down?' Shani took the chair he brought forward for her.

'You're going on your holidays soon,' she said awkwardly. 'Is it to your home?'

'I haven't a home, Shani.' So quiet the statement, and containing a hint of censure not unmixed with yearning. She felt guilty. Why, she thought with a quick frown, should both the men in her life produce in her this feeling of blame? 'I'm going to the island of Cos. Do you know it?'

She lost her apathy and a light of eagerness entered her eyes.

'The Greek island? Of course I know it.' Cos, birth-place of Hippocrates, the 'Father of Medicine'.

'You've been there?'

She shook her head.

'I hope to go some time – in fact I must go.'

'For what reason?' he asked, faintly smiling.

She smiled in response.

'To see the Asclepion, naturally. I expect everyone working in medicine has a desire to go there.'

'The Asclepion ... Hippocrates' hospital. Did you know a centre's being built there where doctors from all over the world can meet and confer?'

'But how wonderful!' Her eyes glowed. 'There couldn't be a more suitable site in the whole world for a centre such as that.'

'Most certainly there couldn't.' A long pause; Shani felt a tenseness creeping over her, but was totally unprepared for her husband's next words. 'Why don't you come with me, Shani?'

A quick intake of her breath, a vision leaping unbidden to her mind – the little island of Cos, and Andreas for company....

'That's quite impossible, you know it is.'

'Can you give me one good reason why you find it quite impossible?' Andreas looked steadily at her and a flush deepened the colour in her cheeks. She was thrown into disorder, staggered by the knowledge that the idea of going with her husband had not been instantly dismissed from her mind.

'It wouldn't be right, Andreas,' she whispered.

'You're my wife, Shani,' he murmured, and at that

she shook her head emphatically. 'We would go only as friends,' he added on noticing her gesture.

'Friends?' Remembering his savagery, his impassioned desire for her, she searched his face intently. What she saw there could not be misread. His word was his bond; he would not break it.

'I – I—' Her lovely eyes continued to regard him, dark with uncertainty. 'My holidays don't – don't coincide with yours.' Feeble words, and totally unconvincing. What had come over her?

'I believe yours start three days after mine. I could wait for you.' Could she be imagining things – or was there really a hint of pleading in his voice? She recalled his admission that he had searched for her, and she wondered at the personality of this dark Greek who was beginning to loom large in her thoughts, despite her efforts to thrust his image out. But it was becoming impossible – in fact, he often occupied her mind to the exclusion of all else – and most certainly to the exclusion of Brian, on whom until recently all her dreams of the future had centred.

'We couldn't . . . the gossip. . . .'

'No one need know.' Those words were drawn from him reluctantly, and Shani wondered why, if he still wanted his wife, he should be having an affair with Lydia. But was it an affair? The hospital staff believed so, and yet Shani had never felt fully convinced.

'People would know; we couldn't keep a thing like that secret. Why, we would both want to talk about it on our return.' What was the matter with her? she asked herself again. The idea of taking a holiday with Andreas was quite out of the question!

'For my part, Shani, I wouldn't care – but you—' For

the merest second she saw the dark venom of jealousy in his eyes before he continued, 'You have this young man, this Brian whom you believe you can marry, despite my firm assertion that you'll never gain your freedom. And so,' he went on hastily as if he feared his words had lost him ground, 'we must keep our secret.'

Silently she sipped her drink, more bewildered and uncertain than ever. To go on holiday with another man while Brian was away?

'No,' she whispered fiercely. 'I can't go with you. Please drop the whole idea!'

A tenseness had enveloped him, but now he relaxed, leaning back in his chair. He was like a man who had staked and lost, and a greyness crept under his skin, mingling with the deep rich bronze which was partly inherent, and partly acquired from exposure to the sun.

'As you wish, Shani, so it must be,' he sighed, and drank deeply from his glass.

'I'm sorry. . . .' That feeling of guilt again. How she wished she could fly somewhere – far from these two men who were tearing her very soul apart. Suddenly she frowned. Was Brian really important in this drama? His rôle had gradually become a minor one . . . with the light slowly but surely focusing on Andreas. In an agony of indecision she pushed a trembling hand through her hair. 'I'm sorry,' she said again, fighting desperately to take what she firmly believed was the honourable course. 'It's quite unthinkable that we should go away together.'

'You've already made that clear,' he said, and to her surprise his voice was lacking in the harshness she expected to discover there. He turned, smiling, as Lydia approached them.

'May I join you?' Her glance at Shani was perfunctory; she had eyes only for Andreas. But presently he rose, saying he must have a word with Matron, and Shani was left alone with the girl who obviously cherished hopes of becoming Andreas's wife. Silence reigned between them until at last Lydia said abruptly, 'You and Mr. Manou were very engrossed. Was it work you were discussing?'

So transparent, thought Shani with an uncharitableness quite foreign to her nature.

'It wasn't work,' she replied non-committally.

Lydia bristled and walked away, crossing the room to join Andreas and Matron.

Shani remained where she was, having no desire for company while her mind was in such chaos. Nevertheless, she smiled when Jenny came up a few minutes later.

'Can't leave him alone!' Jenny flopped into the chair vacated by Andreas, her eyes on Lydia, who was now alone with Andreas. 'No one here believes she'll ever catch him, but I'm not so sure.'

'Not sure?' A strange blockage came into Shani's throat. 'Have you some particular reason for saying that?'

'Well, she's always hanging round him, but for another thing she's actually suggested she should go on holiday with him. What do you think of that for brazenness?'

Shani's lashes fluttered; she said quietly,

'How do you know she suggested going away with him?'

'Heard her, just now.'

'What did she say?'

'To quote her exact words, she said, "Andreas, I've been thinking – I'd love to visit Cos, so why shouldn't

74

we go together?" '

'Mr. Manou – what did he say to that?' The words came with difficulty owing to the tightness in Shani's throat.

'I don't know; I couldn't just stand there and listen to their conversation. The bit I told you I only heard in passing.'

Would Andreas agree to Lydia's proposal? It was feasible. After all, it wouldn't be much fun going alone. . . . But why should I care if they go together? It's only a few weeks since I was hoping Andreas would fall in love with her and agree to an annulment. A few weeks, yes, but so much seemed to have happened to her in that time. Conscious of a dull ache in the region of her heart, Shani glanced across to where the two were standing, deep in conversation. Planning their holiday . . . ?

Why shouldn't she go with her husband? The question, repeated over and over again on the day following the party, seemed gradually to invite only one answer, but still Shani hesitated, and perhaps after all she would have fought against her ever-increasing desire had not Lydia come up to her in the village *taverna* that evening. Shani had called to collect a bottle of wine ordered by Jenny and of course the proprietor pressed her to have a coffee.

'Sister Reeves,' began Lydia without preamble as she took a chair opposite to Shani, 'about last evening. Your manner with me was abrupt to the point of rudeness. I would have you remember that I have a certain measure of authority at the hospital and, therefore, respect must be extended to me.'

'Your father has authority, yes,' Shani owned readily, her temper rising. 'But as for you—' She stopped and shrugged, moving her hand from the table as the coffee was placed before her.

'I'm afraid your head is becoming a little swelled by the interest your boss takes in you,' snapped Lydia. 'But for your own good I advise you not to take that interest seriously. It's entirely professional.'

Shani's eyes glinted; she felt an almost irrepressible urge to blurt out the whole truth, just for the pleasure of witnessing Lydia's amazement and consternation, but instead she casually remarked,

'It would almost seem you had grounds for that assertion?'

'I have,' declared Lydia on impulse. 'Mr. Manou and I are practically engaged. In fact,' she added, lowering her lids to veil her expression, 'I believe we shall be announcing our engagement immediately on his return from Cos.'

The stupid girl, thought Shani with contempt. All this was wishful thinking; Andreas might be interested in Lydia, but he was still adamant regarding his marriage. Again Shani felt the temptation to tell this girl the truth, but all she said was,

'From that I could infer that you were going away together.' For the first time in her life she was behaving like a spiteful little cat, Shani told herself, but this woman did bring out the worst in her.

'We probably shall be,' came the swift retort, but Shani knew the words were rashly spoken and that already Lydia regretted them. Nevertheless, while on the one hand it would appear that Andreas had not yet agreed to take Lydia, on the other hand the girl still believed there was a possibility of his doing so.

Lydia and Andreas together for two weeks. . . .

76

Not much debating and uncertainty after that. Driven by some force stronger either than caution or conscience, Shani called at her husband's house and told him she had changed her mind and was willing to accompany him to Cos. He had been sitting alone, but there was no sign of a book or newspaper and Shani knew instinctively he had been deeply engrossed in thought. But at her words, breathlessly spoken even before he had invited her to sit down, his face cleared miraculously and with the disappearance of the tired lines he once more became inordinately handsome.

'What brought about this change of mind?' he asked a few minutes later as he handed her a drink.

Naturally she could not tell him, but even as she thought of Lydia Shani did begin to wonder if she had been wholly influenced by the conversation at the *taverna*. Perhaps she would in the end have succumbed to her undeniable longing and allowed her conscience to go hang.

'I like the idea of a visit to Cos,' she murmured, shyness creeping over her.

His brows lifted quizzically.

'That's the only reason?'

'Andreas,' she whispered, 'you do mean it's as friends?' She clasped her glass; he relieved her of it and, placing it on the table, took possession of both her hands.

'It's as you want it, my dear.' He looked steadily into her eyes. 'I'm to have your company for two whole weeks; I must not ask for more.'

She bit her lip, amazed to discover herself fighting the tears. Could it be that he loved her? How odd that the idea had never previously occurred to her, she mused as with a flash of memory she heard her father say, after

77

describing how he had fallen in love with her mother on sight, 'And it will be the same with you, Shani. The man will come one wonderful day; he'll see you, and know that you are his.'

She looked at her hands, held lightly in those strong brown fingers, her heart beating far too quickly as she grappled with this new idea, repelling it, refusing to accept it as a revelation. It was not love that had prompted so callous an ultimatum – how could it be? Desire, the primitive urge to possess – this only had been in his mind on that fateful day. If he had loved her he could have told her so, and courted her in the normal way; there was no necessity for that dastardly act of compulsion. And if he loved her now he could still tell her so— But no, he could not, believing as he did that she desired only her freedom so that she could marry someone else. But he did not love her, so why these musings? His desire, though, had obviously waned and as she again returned her gaze to his the tumult within her died and she smiled at him serenely.

'I'm really looking forward to it – now that I've made up my mind.'

He kissed her hands and let them go.

'We'll have a wonderful time ... a time to remember.'

The hotel was on the sea front, high above a golden beach – a lonely beach, it being too late in the year for tourists in any large numbers. Shani's room, next to her husband's, faced the sea, and a tingling of excitement swept through her as she stared out of the window. Placid and enticing lay the blue Aegean while in the distance, half hidden by a purple mist, lay the moun-

78

tains of Turkey, with glistening here and there a cluster of village houses, white against the tree-clad hills.

They had arrived only that morning, and although it was early October the sea was warm and inviting and Shani fell eagerly in with her husband's suggestion that they should begin their holiday by spending the first day on the beach, giving them the chance to 'unwind', as he put it. He was down on the sands already, on the private stretch of beach that ran from the hotel to the sea.

'You couldn't have unpacked,' she said on eventually joining him. 'You didn't have time.'

'I left the boy doing it. Didn't you ask the maid to do yours?' He lay on his side, looking up at her from behind dark glasses.

'It was a man. I couldn't very well ask him to unpack for me.'

'Of course you couldn't.' He got up, tall and lithe and very brown. A surgeon must always be in perfect condition, and Andreas certainly gave the impression of health. 'Ready for a swim?'

She nodded, and let her wrap fall on to the large towel Andreas had spread out on the sands. Seconds later they were in the water.

'It's wonderful!' She was in a dream, living in a world far distant from reality. But then hadn't she read somewhere that Cos was a small piece of paradise itself? And for two whole weeks she would dwell in this paradise. She meant to enjoy it, to laugh and be happy with her husband ... the husband she no longer feared.

After lunch they returned to the beach, and in the evening they dined and danced at the hotel. All windows were thrown wide open and through them drifted the breeze, warmed by its passage over the sea and perfumed by oleanders and jasmine growing in the hotel gardens below.

It was two o'clock in the morning when at last Shani reluctantly admitted to being tired.

'Good night ... my lovely wife.' Lightly Andreas kissed her brow and without another word he left her, entering his room and pushing the door to behind him.

Shani was still at her own door when the latch clicked into place.

The following day they went up to the Asclepion by taxi, but what few visitors there were seemed to have bicycles and when Shani remarked on this Andreas told her that cycling had always been popular with visitors to the island.

'The roads are all so good, as you can see, and as they're lined with flowering trees and shrubs I should imagine it's quite pleasant to cycle.'

'Do they hire them?' she asked, and he nodded, his eyes kindling with amusement as he awaited what was to come. 'Could we ...' She shook her head. Andreas on a bicycle! 'You wouldn't like it, of course.'

'On the contrary, I should thoroughly enjoy it. One doesn't often have the opportunity of such healthy exercise.'

'Shall I wait?' asked the taxi driver on reaching the archaeological site.

'I don't think so; we'll be here a long time.' Andreas turned to Shani. 'Must I tell him to come back or shall we walk? It's up to you.'

'It's not really far, and it's downhill. Let's walk, shall we?' How natural it all was – Andreas casually consulting her and she stating her preference. Just like a

80

normal married couple, she was thinking, and as she smiled to herself Andreas happened to glance down at her.

'What was that for?'

'What . . .?'

'The smile? You know what I'm talking about.'

Her eyes were suddenly lowered evasively, but a gentle hand under her chin brought her head up again.

'I w-was thinking,' she stammered.

'About what?'

A little selfconscious laugh, and then a shrug of resignation.

'I was thinking we sound really married.'

His eyes opened wide.

'We are really married, my dear,' came the gentle but firm reminder. 'I said this holiday would be a time to remember, and I intend it to be just that. But it's only a truce, and if when it's over you still want your freedom we shall be right back where we began.' He released her chin, but she continued to look at him, her eyes large and round, her lips parted and faintly trembling. 'You're my wife, Shani. I'll never let you go.'

So the softness, the hints of amused indulgence she had encountered since leaving Cyprus were only a small part of his make-up. Basically he was inflexible and adamant, a man whose traits of mastery would ever be invincible. She must never forget that, he was telling her.

'Come,' he said, taking her hand and giving it a little squeeze, 'whatever is to face us in the future can be dealt with when it comes. For the present – no hint of disunity must mar one moment of this holiday.'

Whatever is to face us in the future. . . . Shani's

heartbeats quickened, for she grasped a subtle warning in those softly spoken words.

'Andreas . . .?'

'My dear?' His fingers were strong round hers as he steered her leisurely towards the hospital of Hippocrates, for the most part reconstructions, and some columns that had been re-erected after having been brought hurtling down by the natural tremors of the earth. 'What is it?'

'Nothing,' she smiled. 'Nothing at all.'

A short while later as they wandered on to the Sanctuary of Asclepius, the Greek god of healing and medicine, Shani asked a trifle anxiously if Andreas was conversant with the history of the site, as there appeared to be no guide available. 'I know a little,' she added, 'but not enough to say what everything is.'

'I think I know most of the history. Between us we should manage. I like to avoid guides if possible, because where you get guides you automatically get tourists.'

As with all the Greek sanctuaries the site was superb, the shrine having been built in the sacred forest of Apollo, four centuries before Christ. All around were giant cypresses and palms, oleander bushes and shrubs of the scarlet hibiscus, while in the far distance was the tree-dotted plain sweeping down to the Strait of Halicarnassus, and beyond that could be seen the purple shores of Asia.

'There are three levels,' Andreas told her as they began mounting the steps. 'The top one was built first, so we'll begin there.' Still retaining her hand, he seemed to be supplying gentle assistance, even though Shani did not require it. More wide stone steps led up to the Temple of Asclepius, ancestor of Hippocrates and himself descended from Apollo the sun-god.

'I can't differentiate between myth and fact,' complained Shani with a frown. 'If Asclepius was a god and Hippocrates a man then how could they have been related?'

Andreas laughed.

'They weren't, but the ancient Greeks liked to think they were. And as there was no one to argue the point it was generally accepted that Hippocrates was a descendant of the god of healing. Remember, Hippocrates' methods were so new and revolutionary that the ancient Greeks would automatically attribute supernatural powers to him.'

'Yes, I suppose so. And what's so incredible is that his ideas, introduced over two thousand years ago, are accepted today.'

'Fresh air and simple food, healthy exercise and plenty of rest—' He shook his head. 'You're absolutely right, his methods were very twentieth-century in tone.'

They fell silent, both musing on the life of that venerated man who by his genius and intuitive skill gave to the world the ideal physician. One of the discoverers of the fundamental truth – the most vital and significant principle that within the human body there exists a natural physician employed in the task of preservation – Hippocrates was ever conscious of the fact that the success of the physician depended on the assistance of this *vis-medicatrix* of nature.

'He was the first man to overcome witchcraft and superstition.' Shani murmured her thoughts aloud, but Andreas seemed not to hear and she lapsed into silence again, thinking of the growth of the hospital and of how stricken people travelled from all parts of the ancient world to be cured in this environment of isolation and peace. Hippocrates himself studied at the Asclepion, later becoming a wandering physician, increasing his knowledge and scientific skill before returning to his native island of Cos.

There he built a splendid temple to the god of healing and soon his hospital was famed as being the first medical faculty in which students could study medicine scientifically. Under his direction the Asclepion became a temple of art as well as a place of healing and worship, the great doctor's theory being that the equilibrium of a man's inner world was fundamental to his health. So by Hippocrates' direction artistic creations were introduced to supplement, and harmonize with, the natural beauties of the site. Bronze and marble statues embellished the grounds, the most magnificent being the statues of Asclepius and Apollo, and the beautiful Aphrodite of Apelles. Through his teachings and revolutionary theories Hippocrates laid the foundations of scientific thought that was to influence medical men all over the world two and a half thousand years later.

'He was certainly a wonderful man.' Andreas's belated response to his wife's remark came at last. 'Just think, even his oath survives, sworn by every graduate in medicine.'

The Hippocratic Oath. . . . Mentally Shani repeated some of the sentences. 'The regimen I adopt shall be for the benefit of my patients according to my ability and judgment, and not for their hurt or wrong, and never shall I do harm to anyone. I will prescribe no deadly drug that may cause death though it be asked of

me. I will preserve the purity of my life and my art. . . .'
Shani glanced up at her husband. His eyes were narrowed against the glare as he picked out what was left of the famous Temple of Asclepius. So tall and straight . . . clean and healthy both in mind and body.

Could such a man indulge in an affair? Was Lydia really *that* sort of a friend, as some of the staff at Loutras believed? Shani already doubted this, and now. . . . 'I will preserve the purity of my life'. Greek he might be, and amorous by nature, but as she watched him, lost in a mental reconstruction of the ancient scene, Shani could not believe he would ever for one moment forget that oath.

'Just look at these steps—' He let go of her hand as he gestured. 'Black marble.'

'They're beautiful. They must have brought the marble from a great distance.'

Andreas shook his head. The metamorphic rocks of the island's mountain range contained deposits of this very attractive type of marble, he informed her, adding,

'They were lucky, as marble was so important in the days of this magnificent architecture and statue-building.'

Apart from the steps, a few traces of a portico and several columns, nothing remained of the wonderful Doric Temple of Asclepius, and Andreas spoke sadly of the island's many earthquakes.

They wandered about the ruins, mere vestiges of a long-decayed splendour, picking out foundations of what could have been doctors' houses and nurses' apartments.

'Did the patients have to pay for their treatment?' asked Shani as the thought occurred to her.

'No. But in the Temple of Asclepius there was an altar of thanksgiving. People placed money in the box provided. The money was for the god, but of course it went towards the upkeep of the hospital.'

On the next level was a little Ionic temple, relics of a Roman villa, and part of another great temple. Shani had stopped to gaze over the enchanting landscape and when, a little ahead, Andreas turned, it was to see her standing there, looking small and lovely against the gleaming white marble of the tall Corinthian column. Six other columns rose in splendour to become outlined against a flawless Grecian sky, while framed between them in the near distance were the graceful tapering cypress trees, unswaying in the stillness of the perfumed air.

'Stand still,' he said, bringing out his camera. It clicked; Andreas smiled his permission for her to move and she came up to him. He closed the camera case with what seemed quite unnecessary care and for some obscure reason a lump rose in Shani's throat. She tried to read his expression, but his face wore its customary impassive aspect and his eyes were hidden behind the dark glasses he had just a moment ago put on.

On the lowest level, which they presently reached on descending the wide staircase, the healing spring still gushed forth as it had in Hippocrates' day, and as they were by this time thirsty and hot they both drank from its sparkling waters. Andreas dried her hands, and then his own, and she suddenly felt close in a way she would never have believed possible.

'Tell me when you're tired, Shani, won't you?' They were at the foot of some ancient narrow steps, having halted, neither quite certain if it were permissible to mount them, as they were some distance from the main buildings on the site and seemed to lead only to a wooded enclosure. 'I can go on and on, but you – I don't want you to get tired.' A hint of concern in his voice that could not be missed, and a tenderness in his eyes as he looked anxiously at her.

She shook her head, happiness flooding over her . . . a happiness that set her wondering what the outcome of this holiday would be.

'Possessed as I am of a woman's curiosity,' she returned with a gay little laugh, 'I *must* see what's at the top of these steps.'

'Then here goes,' agreed Andreas, responding to her mood. 'If we're trespassing, and we're caught, we'll just have to plead ignorance and apologize nicely.'

A dark, thickly-wooded glade met their eyes as they reached the top of the steps. Here was stored masses of broken masonry excavated from all over the surrounding areas of this fantastic archaeological site. All was so still, and as they trod between the broken columns and statue bases Shani felt herself becoming a part of this sombre, austere solitude.

'It's sort of – creepy,' she whispered, unconsciously moving closer to his side. 'Do you feel it?'

'It is rather spooky,' he agreed, slipping an arm about her shoulders. 'But there's nothing to be afraid of. The overgrown vegetation keeps out the light, that's all.'

'It could be the cemetery,' she suggested, looking round. 'I suppose some of the patients were buried here.'

'Not in the sacred precincts. No one was allowed to die here.'

She stared, bewildered.

'There must have been deaths. Even the great Hippocrates couldn't effect a cure in every case.'

'When it was discovered that a patient had an incurable disease his or her people were sent for and asked to remove the patient.'

'That was rather callous, wasn't it?'

'To our way of thinking, yes. But the Asclepion was a shrine, remember, and people were never permitted to die within the precincts of a shrine.' A fairly modern building appeared through a break in the trees and they directed their steps towards it. The door was wide open and they entered, Shani giving a little gasp as she glanced around her.

'What are these? Just look, wonderful tablets, and all covered with writing. There must be hundreds!'

This was quite true; the walls were covered with these tablets, and many more were stacked on the floor. They were mostly in white marble, with the writing as clear as the day it was etched into the stone.

'Wonderful!' echoed Andreas. 'These must have been buried during one of the early earthquakes, because they've not suffered any weathering at all.'

'What do they say?'

As Andreas read the ancient Greek writing he shook his head now and then in a gesture of amazement.

'These,' he told her, tapping one of the tablets, 'are letters of thanks to the doctors and nurses.'

She stared unbelievingly.

'Just as it is now. I often receive a letter of thanks, and I expect you do too?'

He nodded.

'They're so beautifully done. Look at this one – see how the edges have been scrolled.'

'What does it say?'

'It's to a doctor, thanking him for the cure effected – "for taking away my affliction which for years I endured". The writer then goes on to inform the doctor that a suitable offering has been placed on the altar in the Temple of Asclepius.'

Wonderingly she examined several of the other tablets before saying, in a rather awed little voice,

'Imagine us reading that letter, after two and a half thousand years.' She stopped and frowned. 'It makes you realize, Andreas, just how short your life is.'

He was at the other end of the room, scanning a particularly beautifully executed panel, but at her words he turned and, coming back to her, he placed gentle hands on her shoulders and looked deeply into her eyes.

'Life is short, my dear, and therefore exceedingly precious. We should not waste a moment of it.' Grave words, spoken so gently ... and his touch, so tender on her arms, filled her with an emotion she had never known before, and in a flash of reminiscence she saw those five years that had passed since her marriage – five years that could have been spent as the wife of this man whose wisdom and gentleness affected her in so profound a way that the unkindness to which he had subjected her seemed to fade into insignificance. He smiled, playfully flicked her cheek and said lightly,

'How serious we are! Let us turn our attention to the good things of life. Are you hungry?'

'Starving,' she laughed, and with a totally unconscious gesture she tucked her arm through his and together they descended the steps and made for the gate leading to the road back into town.

CHAPTER FIVE

THEY had intended lunching in the city of Cos, which was the capital of the island, but on the way down the lively *bouzouki* music drifting to them from a roadside *taverna* drew them to its open door. Two men were dancing the *soûska*, while others clapped in rhythm to the music.

'How about it?' queried Andreas. 'Local colour – or a luxury hotel? Yours is the choice.'

'Local colour every time!'

He frowned at that.

'Not every time. Luxury's nice for a change.'

They entered, stepping to one side of the dancers, and chose two large red mullet from the variety of freshly-caught fish on display under the glass counter.

The meal was eventually brought to them outside, where they were sitting at a table under the vines. They drank *retzina* with their food and Turkish coffee afterwards. They were stared at and discussed; another dance was performed especially for them. It was very different from the first, with the man singing a melancholy song as he repeatedly fell down and rose again in a series of despairing yet gracefully executed movements.

'I've never seen this dance before.' On first going to Cyprus Shani had attended Greek dancing lessons at the gymnasium, and after a great deal of perseverance she was now regarded as an expert. Most of the Greek dances she knew, and she was quite sure this particular one had never been performed in Cyprus. She turned to her husband, noticing the odd expression in his eyes as he watched intently the sad movements of the slim and supple performer. 'What is he doing?'

'He's from Kalymnos – another island not far from Cos. Most of the men are engaged in sponge-diving; that, and a little agriculture, are the only means of livelihood there. But sponge-diving's a highly danger-ous occupation and men frequently suffer paralysis from the under-water pressures. This particular dance belongs to Kalymnos and is rooted in the conditions there. The song's very sad, expressing the man's grief at his inability to perform the dance from which at one time he had derived the greatest ecstasy.'

'And the movements symbolize the paralytic diver attempting to dance as before – when he was perfect in body?'

Andreas nodded.

'He keeps falling down, as you can see, but insists on continuing the dance which he once so loved and per-formed with extreme grace and skill.' The dance ended to loud handclapping from everyone, and as the man would have sat down Andreas beckoned to him, in-viting him to join them.

'What are you drinking?' The man told him and when the order was given Andreas said, 'You're from Kalymnos, obviously. How do you come to be in Cos?'

'I married a girl from Cos, so I live here.' The man's English was good and Andreas remarked on it. 'I learnt at school.' The man shook his head. 'It's not as good as I would wish; it's difficult to practise because my wife and her family speak only Greek.'

'Were you a sponge-diver?'

The young man nodded.

'I started at seventeen and for six years I did this work.' He frowned. 'I was glad when I found this girl who has a house and much land from her father. We grow many mandarins and some tobacco also. It's a better life and I am very lucky.'

'Where's your wife now?' There was a hint of amusement in Andreas's eye as he caught Shani's glance.

'Working,' the man replied gravely. 'She toils hard on the land. She is a good girl.'

'Tell me about the sponge-diving,' put in Shani eagerly. 'My husband had been explaining your dance to me—' She stopped, astounded at the natural way the word had slipped out. Her cheeks reddened and she deliberately avoided Andreas's gaze, but instinctively she knew that his eyes were fixed intently upon her, his surprise as great as her own.

The young man explained how the boats went out from the harbour at Kalymnos every April, sailing to the north coast of Africa, where the sponges were of especially fine quality.

'All the ships sail away together and it's a wonderful sight,' he admitted, 'but you wave good-bye to your relatives knowing you will not see them for five months. And also you know that some of you will come back maimed, and that some of you will not come back at all, for always men are lost on these trips.' He went on to describe the ceremony at the harbour before the fleet sailed. There was a dinner provided by the Municipality, to which every member of a fisherman's family was invited, even small children attending. All the priests of Kalymnos would be there and the bishop would bless the boats and prayers would be said for their safe return. 'The Easter ceremony is solemn and sad,' the man continued. 'But the one in September is much more joyful.'

'But even then some people will be sad – when they know their men are maimed, or even dead.' Shani spoke softly, almost to herself.

'Yes, of course. That is what used to spoil it for me, because always I would think of my friends who were crippled or dead.'

'And,' said Shani, a note of indignation creeping into her voice, 'I suppose you don't even get well paid for this hazardous work?'

'Yes, we do. We receive very high wages, and this is paid to us in advance because we have to leave our families provided for.'

Andreas nodded musingly.

'The captain of the ship pays you this money?'

'That's right. He gets a loan from the Government.'

'And on your return the sponges are sold to the merchants, I suppose?'

'Yes; they're sold by weight, but must be dried first.'

The man had drained his glass and Andreas ordered him another drink.

'Do the sponges move around all over the sea?' Shani wanted to know, wondering why she had never before thought about the sponge she used in her bath.

'No, they're fastened to the rocks and have to be

dragged off. Sometimes the draught is strong and then the work of dragging them off the rocks is very hard.' He grinned ruefully. 'You haven't much time, either, if you're using your own breath.'

'You use your own breath!' Shani's eyes opened wide in surprise, but Andreas was merely nodding.

'Some men go down without diving-suits, but for the most part suits are used nowadays.'

'Yes. . . .' The man agreed with this, although reluctantly. 'But men still use their own breath quite a lot.' He looked at Shani. 'And do you know what they do to save time and get to the bottom quickly?' She shook her head and he added, 'They hold a huge boulder so that it carries them down at a great speed.'

She shuddered, convinced that every time she bought a sponge she would think of the dangers faced by the brave men of Kalymnos.

'Wasn't he interesting?' she said a short while later as they were leaving the *taverna*. 'I'm so glad we met him.'

'So am I.' A small pause and then Andreas laughed. 'When he talked about the boulder I thought we would be sure to hear the story of the man who was swallowed by a shark.'

'Swallowed by a shark?'

'The man concerned was in the habit of carrying a large piece of rock in order to speed up his descent. On this particular occasion he – and the rock – went straight into the open jaws of a shark. The impact of the rock on the shark's stomach caused it to vomit and out shot the man. He came up with scratches on his arms as proof of this adventure, and instantly became famous.'

'It isn't true, of course,' asserted Shani with a laugh. 'It just couldn't be!'

'Don't, my child, ever say that on Kalymnos – should you ever go there. Everybody believes it. As I've said, the man became famous.'

Don't, my child. . . . Shani looked up, seeing Andreas only as her husband. He was young and almost gay – not at all like the exacting, intolerant superior who snapped out orders to her in the theatre. But how different he was in *every* way, now that he was on vacation and free from the cares and anxieties of his work. During those years of separation, whenever his image had passed like a glimpse of some fleeting dream through her mind, she had known only revulsion, seeing a dark foreigner in her room, impervious to her childish entreaties. But now he was fast taking on a very different aspect and often she would recall his saying that if she stayed with him one night, she would remain with him for ever. Her musings were brought to an end as, on reaching the flower-bedecked town of Cos she found herself being guided over to where the bicycles could be hired.

'We'll not have them today,' Andreas decided. 'It's too late, but we'll make arrangements to call for them tomorrow morning.'

They hired the cycles almost every day after that, and rode to several villages on the island. But for two whole days they stayed in the capital, exploring the antiquities.

'I've never seen so many in so small an area!' exclaimed Shani one day as they rode towards the ancient gymnasium. The approach was along an avenue, on both sides of which were standard oleanders, no more than a few feet apart. Gardens dripped with exotic flowers thriving in the sun, their heady perfumes carried by a light breeze blowing in from the sea. 'It's an archaeologist's paradise!' Dismounting, they propped their bicycles against a tree and wandered on to the site, there being no one to take the money as it was so late in the season. 'How do they come to have so many ancient sites, Andreas? They're all around the town.'

'The last earthquake was as recent as 1933, remember, and although this was catastrophic it did lay bare much treasure that, through the ages, had been built upon. The new town avoided these sites, so enabling the archaeologists to bring to light all these wonderful things we are now seeing.'

They explored the gymnasium and ancient agora, found the temples of Apollo and Venus, admired the beautiful mosaics unearthed by the Italian archaeologists, and came at last to the amphitheatre, where they sat resting under the warm sun and eating pomegranates picked by Andreas from a tree above their heads.

On the third day's exploration they were well away from the town, intent on finding a special eating-place which the hotel receptionist recommended to them, when suddenly Shani jumped off her bicycle.

'More antiquities! And out here in the wilds. Do you think we're allowed to go in?'

'There isn't a soul about to prevent us.' Which was true; they had miles of open country to themselves.

The fallen columns were practically covered with vegetation; apart from the heads of three marble lions there was little else to be seen. But for some reason

Shani bent down and began dragging at the roots of the rough grass and other weeds growing on the field.

'Help me,' she begged excitedly at last. 'There's something hard under here!'

'You are aware you're breaking the law?' he warned, but complied with her request. 'I do believe you're right. You've found something,' he added a moment later.

'I was bound to; it's an unexcavated site we've discovered.'

'Not discovered, my dear. This site's known, naturally.'

'Oh, yes, I agree, but it hasn't yet been excavated. I wonder why?'

'Lack of funds, probably. Look at the numerous sites in Cyprus that are unexcavated because of lack of money.'

Shani was engrossed in her task; carefully they removed the roots and then, even more carefully, the soil. Presently Shani gave a little gasp.

'A beautiful mosaic,' she breathed. 'Andreas, we must tell someone!'

He smiled at that and continued for some moments to uncover more of the mosaic.

'The authorities know this is here—'

'How can they? We've just found it.'

'After someone else has already found it – you can be quite sure of that.'

'But this vegetation – the mosaic's been completely buried until now.'

'I think there's no doubt at all that this site's been surveyed. Look at the columns; we're not the only people who've noticed them.' He threw her a glance of amusement and stood up, brushing the soil from his hands. 'No, Shani, we haven't made some marvellous discovery. This site awaits excavation and meanwhile it's hoped no meddlesome tourists will start probing—' He broke off, laughing at her crestfallen expression. 'Or removing vegetation that has obviously been allowed to grow over the site – even encouraged to do so, I should imagine. Come, we must cover it up again.'

'Oh. . . .' Thoroughly disappointed, she turned from him to gaze down at the exquisite picture of birds and flowers which was only a small section of what could very well prove to be a large and valuable mosaic. 'All the same,' she said, brightening, 'this is a marvellous island. It must be overflowing with treasure. I think it's a wonderful place!'

A week later she uttered a similar exclamation. They were alone in the hotel garden, strolling under a magical sky with all around them the perfumed air, soft and warm. Suddenly Shani felt herself drawn close to her husband, heard his gentle persuasive whisper in her ear:

'It is a wonderful place, my Shani . . . a wonderful place for a honeymoon.' Instantly she stiffened, and twisted away, thrown into confusion. 'I'm sorry,' he said quietly. 'Forget it.'

She stared up at him, her face flushed. She thought, 'Had I not twisted away he would have kissed me.'

'I – Andreas—'

'Let's go in; it's late. Don't trouble your lovely head about it,' he added, noting her expression. 'I said nothing would mar this holiday, and I meant it.' He took her hand in his and they walked in silence back to the hotel.

'Andreas, I can't—' She had been going to tell him of her confusion, and that she could not think clearly, but he interrupted with,

'I said don't trouble about it. We've only four days left, so let's be happy.' He smiled at her, no sign of anger in his eyes. 'Didn't I say at first it was going to be a time to remember?'

She nodded, but when her expression did not change he looked sternly at her and ordered her to smile. She obliged, and quite unable to control the impulse, Andreas bent his head and kissed her on the lips.

But from that day his gaiety and lightheartedness was a veneer, and Shani was quick to sense this. Underneath he seemed almost to carry some weight of grief. He was like a man who had fought, desperately yet honourably ... and lost. She tried to approach him, attempted on a couple of occasions to steer the conversation into lines where she could tell him of her growing uncertainty, could convey without the actual embarrassment of words that she was feeling differently about her marriage, but that he must be patient with her, allowing her a little more time because, after all, she was really only just beginning to know him, through this holiday. But each time he brushed her off, believing, she felt sure, that she was annoyed at his suggestion that they make these last few days their honeymoon. And so it was with her confession still unmade that they returned to Loutras where, after having spent an idyllic fortnight together dining and dancing, swimming in the warm sea and exploring the island, they drifted once more into the old relationship.

Andreas talked of his holiday to his colleagues; Shani on the other hand was supposed to have been staying with friends in the Karpas and as she had stayed there several times before, her friends merely inquired if she had enjoyed her holiday. Shani did not know what her feelings for Andreas were, but intruding persistently into her mind were his gravely-spoken words, 'Think about it, Shani, for we've a long way to go and the road can be lonely.'

But he did not love her and so for the time being she refused to dwell on the possibility of living with him. Of one thing, however, she was sure; she could not now entertain the idea of marrying Brian, and the sooner she told him so the better. She would be completely honest with him, and hope he would not take it too badly. She also hoped there would not be a scene, but her heart began beating abnormally when on his return to the base at Limassol Brian immediately telephoned her.

'Darling, I'm back! When can I see you? I'm coming up at the weekend. Are you free?'

'Y-yes.' She felt flustered. Her confession could not be made over the telephone – it wouldn't be fair. Also, it would be cowardly, too much like shirking a most disagreeable task. On the other hand it was also unfair to leave Brian in total ignorance, allowing him to look forward eagerly to a happy weekend in her company. In honour bound she was forced to give him some inkling of the break that was to come. But how? With a sudden inspiration she thought of a way of preparing Brian while at the same time leaving the most important fact – that of her own change of heart – until they met. 'Yes, I'm free at the weekend, Brian, but something's happened—'

'Happened?' he interrupted sharply. 'The annulment?'

He himself had provided the opening for her and Shani made use of it.

'Andreas is confident that only he can annul the marriage, because I refused to live with him, and so I probably would never have regained my freedom. However, there's much more to it than that, but I'll tell you about it when I see you.'

'Only—' Brian seemed to have missed completely her last words as he said to himself, 'Only he can annul the marriage, eh?' A long silence followed and then he asked in harsh and wrathful tones, 'Did you know of his confidence before I went away?'

'Yes, Brian, I did.'

'Then why didn't you tell me?'

'I didn't want to upset you, not then. But now—'

'You said he was resigned!'

'No,' she denied hastily. 'I said he seemed a little resigned – but I also said he didn't want to release me.'

'Does this mean there's likely to be a delay?' he inquired after another pause.

Shani hesitated. Although still unwilling to make her full confession over the telephone, she did say, in quiet gentle tones,

'There might not be an annulment, but,' she added hastily as Brian would have interrupted, 'we'll talk at the weekend—' He cut her short with a wrathful exclamation and then said,

'Leave this to me! It's high time I took a hand in this

business. He's not getting away with it!'

'Brian – no!' she put in urgently. 'There's more to it— *Brian!*' she cried frantically, but he had already hung up on her.

She rang him again, fretting at the long delay. At last the operator told her there was no reply.

What did he intend to do? she wondered fearfully. But he would not do anything before seeing her at the weekend, she reassured herself after some thought. In fact, there really wasn't anything he could do, despite his confidently-spoken threat.

CHAPTER SIX

THE hospital at Monikomo occupied a high plateau in the Troodos Mountains between the villages of Pedhoulas and Prodhromos, and a few weeks after Andreas's arrival at Loutras he had been called out to perform an operation there. As at the time the hospital was short-staffed Shani accompanied him and, like Andreas, was appalled at the lack of facilities at a hospital situated in an area where accidents could often happen. Not only was the mountain road narrow and steep, with dangerous bends appearing every few hundred yards, but the region was also a popular winter resort for skiers. However, as Andreas had never again referred to the paucity of equipment, Shani experienced some surprise when, on the morning following Brian's phone call, Andreas summoned her to his room saying he had been in touch by telephone with the young doctor in charge at Monikomo who had readily agreed with Andreas's suggestion that they get together and list essential equipment, and the doctor would then request its installation. Shani and Andreas had met once since the holiday, in the theatre. On that occasion he had been the cool and impassive surgeon, scarcely seeing his wife at all as a person. Now he was almost the same – her superior, curt, unsmiling, and in addition there was a strange tenseness about him as if he were keeping some fury in check. Uneasiness swept over Shani for some vague reason, but eventually she managed to cast it off as Andreas outlined his plans in calm, unemotional tones. He wanted her to go up to Troodos with him, saying she might have some suggestions. This request increased her surprise; she thought it rather odd that he should concern himself with so small a hospital, just as, until he mentioned his 'search' for her, it had amazed her that he should come to work at Loutras after having practised at one of the largest hospitals in London.

'I shall probably be called out on future occasions to operate at Monikomo,' he said as if reading her thoughts, 'so I'm going to see that it becomes better equipped.'

'When are you intending to go up there?' she asked, and he said they would go that very afternoon. At that she looked doubtfully at him. 'It won't give us long – unless you don't mind driving back in the dark.'

A profound silence followed before Andreas said, in an expressionless voice,

'The driving won't trouble me. We'll start out about twelve,' he added, 'and have something to eat on the way.'

They stopped at the village of Lefka for lunch, eating *kebabs* and salads and drinking Turkish coffee. Figs hung from a tree by the restaurant and on seeing her eyes on them Andreas asked Shani if she would like some.

'It's all right.' She was feeling oddly disturbed again because this was not the Andreas she had known on holiday. The change in him was so dramatic that those wonderful days spent on the island of Cos might never have occurred. 'They probably don't want to pick them.'

'Have you ever heard of a Cypriot being reluctant to

pick something if a visitor wanted it? They're honoured when you desire what is theirs.' This was true and she made no further demur. The figs, washed and put into a glass bowl, appeared within minutes and Shani helped herself.

'Ready?' Andreas asked a short while later, glancing at his watch.

'Yes.' That tinge of uneasiness remained and in an effort to throw it off she tried to open a conversation, but Andreas was in an introspective mood and she soon abandoned the attempt, giving her attention to the passing scene.

Leaving behind the orange groves, they entered the foothills of Troodos and then they really climbed, reaching the vast pine forest and often being forced to crawl as the narrow road, cut into the rocky cliffs, snaked its way round the bluffs and spurs until at last they arrived at Pedhoulas. Another mile and a half and their destination was reached.

'That was a very pleasant run.' Reaching across Shani, Andreas opened the door for her. 'I hope you enjoyed it too?'

'I did, very much.' She got out of the car, into an all-embracing silence, into a world of lofty crags and peaks, deserted except for the small building that was the hospital.

'You can talk to Matron while we go round,' Andreas told her as they entered, to be greeted by the matron and a smiling young Greek Cypriot doctor. 'I'll send for you if I need you.'

Shani looked up quickly, but his face was impassive. If I need you. . . . What an odd thing to say. If he had not expected to need her then why was she here?

He did send for her eventually and she made notes, but this was all she did, and the small task could very easily have been done by one of the nurses at the hospital. However, Shani did not attach undue importance to this and when, their work finished, they had afternoon tea with the doctor and matron she took part unconcernedly in the conversation.

On emerging from the hospital entrance they were in an awesome realm of darkness and indistinct shapes, with etched against the deep purple sky the black outline of Mount Olympus, its summit draped in mist.

'It's a hazardous road in the dark,' warned the doctor. 'If you prefer to stay, there's an hotel just above here.'

'Thank you, no.' Taking her arm, Andreas guided Shani to the car, which was out of the line of light from the hospital entrance, Andreas having parked it under a tree. 'I'm not very fond of these off-the-track hotels.'

'Take care, then.' The doctor gave a little laugh. 'A friend of mine counted a hundred and fifty-nine bends on the way down one day. I don't know if that is correct – but it's a difficult road, to say the least.'

The bends were hairpin bends, with a camber often so acute that the car appeared to be travelling on two wheels. They had been on the road about fifteen minutes when Shani, having been lost in thought, suddenly became aware of her surroundings.

'Are you taking a different road?' There was no other road, not from the point at which they had begun their journey. Somewhere, then, Andreas had turned into what was nothing more than a rough mountain track. 'You've missed your way. Shall I get out and guide you back to the road?' It would be difficult, reversing out of this narrow track, she thought apprehensively. He did not speak for a moment and she peered into the gloom. High peaks, the great expanse of pine forest on all sides, the moonless, starless sky above. A towering motionless world with no visible sign of habitation anywhere.

'I have a small villa up here,' he said, straining his eyes in the headlight glare. 'Yes, I see it. I want to call there.'

'I didn't know you had a villa.' Many people had villas in the Troodos. It was quite usual for those who could afford it to spend a couple of months in the mountains during the intense heat of the summer. 'Have you had it long?'

'About six weeks, but I've never used it yet.' The rough gravel crunched beneath the wheels of the car. They had entered a deep forest glade in the most beautiful region of the Marathassa Valley and the track was so narrow that the lowest branches of the trees touched the sides of the car.

'Are we nearly there?'

'We're here now.' The car slid to a standstill and at last Shani could make out the dim shape of the villa. It stood on a tiny ledge cut into one side of the magnificent highland valley.

'It's a wonderful spot.' Shani stood by the car, glancing back and thinking it would have been better if Andreas had called on his way up because the journey back was going to take some considerable time. 'Is it something of importance you have to do?'

No answer. He unlocked the door and within seconds the hall and patio were flooded with light.

'It's very nice.' Shani walked in and looked about her appreciatively. 'You'll find this very useful next summer. People also use these villas in the winter, as we have a ski club up here – but of course you know about it,' she added with an apologetic little laugh.

'It would be a good idea to come up here for winter sports. I must think about it.' There was a sharp click and Shani turned. Andreas had closed the door behind him ... and locked it. Before her startled gaze he dropped the key into his pocket. 'Go on through; the sitting-room's most attractive.'

She stood motionless. Her heart missed a beat and the blackness they had left outside seemed to close in on her, allowing only the mental vision of those moments of terror before she had fled from this dark foreigner whose aim it was to possess her.

'The k-key,' she stammered through the dryness in her throat. 'What are y-you doing?'

He smiled at her, his straight black brows lifting slightly.

'You ran from me once, Shani – and a most humili-ating experience it was for me to find you gone.' A slender brown hand went automatically to his pocket; through the fine linen of his jacket he felt the key. 'That won't happen tonight.'

His manner was one of bland affability, and Shani's fear subsided temporarily, replaced by surprise. Why should he do this to her? – and at this particular time? On the holiday there had been a mere suggestion, fol-lowed by resigned acceptance of her decision. Not that he could have brought force to bear then as he could now, but he had displayed neither anger nor animosity at her evasion of his request that they should make a honeymoon of their last few days on Cos. So why should he suddenly and calculatingly plan to get her in his power?

'Andreas,' she whispered, 'you can't – can't. . . .' Her eyes strayed from the locked door to the shuttered window. Why waste words?

'I can't – what?' He would have taken her hand, but she twisted away. 'What is it that I cannot do?' Still the affability. No intention of frightening her by a show of mastery. She frowned, his action still puzzling her. Why, she asked herself again, had he chosen this particular time? The visit to Monikomo. . . . She felt certain it had been arranged only that very morning, for the sole purpose of getting her here . . . tonight.

Her husband was watching her, trying no doubt to read her thoughts. Her cheeks were hot and her eyes glazed. Fear rose again, but disappointment filled her as well. She had come gradually to trust Andreas, and now a terrible bitterness swept through her. She should have known better than to trust a man capable of adopting such dishonourable means of making her his wife. Despair and dread began to mingle with her bitterness, but she contrived to maintain a composed and defiant front.

'You can't force anything on me! I'm not your wife and never will be, so you can open that door and take me back to Loutras!'

'Not my wife?' His eyes opened wide. 'I seem to recall that we had a most fashionable wedding.'

She moved, to tug at the door handle – a futile action, but she could not just stand there and do nothing.

'Let me out of here!'

Andreas merely regarded her in some amusement and she came away from the door.

'That's far more sensible, Shani—'

'You're a cheat! You cheated me before and you've done it again. I came here in all innocence, believing you were calling at the villa for some valid reason!'

'What more valid reason could I have?' he returned with a laugh. 'This, my most beautiful wife, is to be our honeymoon night. Belated, very, but it could be the more enjoyable for that.'

Her fists clenched.

'You think there'll be no annulment if you keep me here, but—'

'I don't think, my dear, I'm sure.' His voice was a soft snarl, the sudden change taking her by surprise. 'After this night there'll be no more fuss about an annulment, no more threats.'

Threats? How softly he spoke the word, but his mouth was drawn back, revealing his teeth. What was he talking about? She had never once issued threats. But there was nothing to be gained by arguing with him. Instead, she reminded him that Matron and others of the staff at Loutras would look askance at this escapade.

'Petrol trouble,' he replied suavely. 'We had to put up at an hotel.'

'You thought of everything!'

'That didn't take much thinking up.' He stood by the fireplace. It was high and built of stone; the grate was filled with logs, ready for lighting. 'We can have a meal,' he told her matter-of-factly. 'A woman from Pedhoulas comes in to keep the place aired and clean. I rang the Muktar this morning and asked him to give her instructions to stock the refrigerator.'

'I don't want anything to eat!'

'Don't be silly. Of course you must eat.'

Her eyes blazed.

'That's one thing you can't make me do. If I say I won't eat, then I won't!' Angry tears pricked her eyes, but her hands fell to her sides in a little hopeless gesture. What good was she doing, working herself into a frenzy like this? After five years Andreas had won. No use fighting, no use appealing to his sense of compassion or honour. He was a Greek; she his wife. It was all as simple as that.

Stooping, Andreas set a match to the fire, then disappeared into the kitchen. Shani moved over to the window. The long bar-fastener was on the inside, but she did not try to escape. There was not only the window to open but the shutters too, and she was sure her husband would be on the alert for any sound from the sitting-room. Her head began to throb and she put it in her hands. Her decision regarding Brian was her own; the matter of the annulment was now decided for her. She was Andreas's wife and in this state she must remain for the rest of her life.

'Shani.' Her husband's voice came to her and she dropped her hands.

'Yes?'

'Come and help me. I have no idea what to do with this steak.'

Mechanically she moved, entering the kitchen. She seemed to be in a trance, hating her husband and yet acutely aware of her recent admission that the continual intrusion of Andreas into her mind was, to say the least, disturbing.

'It's frozen,' she murmured, picking up the plate of meat.

'We'll have to wait until it thaws.' He glanced at the clock. 'There's plenty of time, I suppose, but can't it be put in the oven as it is?'

She nodded. How utterly unreal this situation was! And how could she have come to accept it, neither fighting him physically nor wounding with her tongue? Fighting him physically ... ? Not much would be gained by an attempt at that, she owned swiftly, seeing those strong and sinewed hands as they worked skilfully and untiringly to save a life.

'It would cook eventually, yes,' she agreed, lifting her eyes to his and finding only softness there.

'Come, then, do your stuff with the onions and other vegetables.'

Suddenly her eyes flashed.

'I've said I'm not hungry!'

'You will be, when you smell the cooking. Here are the carrots and – now let me see – yes, I told Agni to get me a cauliflower. At least, it was on the list I read out to the Muktar. It must be around somewhere.'

'You're very efficient,' she retorted with sarcasm.

'One must eat, my dear.' His dark eyes laughed at her and she turned her back on him. But she prepared the vegetables and soon the casserole was in the oven. She stood by the stove, amazed at her own docility. Yet what sense was there in antagonizing her husband? The ordeal had to be endured, she was quite resigned to that – so why invite trouble for herself by inflaming Andreas?

And so she ate the meal, even though at times the food choked her. And when she had cleared away the dishes and washed them, Andreas took her unre-sistingly into his arms, just holding her at first as if content with the nearness of her.

'I never intended it to be like this, my Shani,' he said after a while. 'I searched for you, hoping that when I found you I'd be able to persuade you to come to me willingly, to live with me and be my wife. But instead you immediately asked for your freedom so that you could marry someone else.' He paused broodingly. 'During the holiday – I hoped—' He broke off, holding her away from him and looking rather sadly into her eyes, but he did not continue. What had he been about to add? With a flash of memory she heard him saying, 'And if, when this holiday is over you still want an annulment. . . .'

If? So he had cherished hopes that by the end of the holiday she would no longer want her freedom. What a strange man he was! Had she not been sure that his only aim was possession she could almost have believed he cared for her. But she *was* sure his only aim was possession.

'You actually hoped for docile surrender?' She looked scornfully at him. 'That you will never bring about. By a detestable threat you forced me into mar-riage and by a trick you've at last managed to achieve your desire. But I'll never be yours, never.'

Strangely, he answered that in quiet and gentle tones.

'You'll be mine, Shani; just for this one night you'll be all my own. I know you'll hate me, but I'm not letting you have that annulment—'

'So you admit at last that I can get it? You said only you were in a position to do so, while all the time knowing I had only to relate the circumstances of the marriage and I'd have had no trouble at all.'

To her surprise he remained unmoved by the interruption, merely saying,

'I haven't admitted anything of the sort. I still maintain that only I can annul the marriage.' He frowned at her, a trifle puzzled. 'You know very well that only I can annul the marriage. You've discussed it with—' He broke off, gritting his teeth. 'Why all this talk? As I've said, after tonight there will be no question of a breakup of our marriage.'

She was outside in the garden when Andreas came from the house. The mountain air, warmed by being drawn through the valley, was nevertheless fresh and clear, and heady with the scent of pines. She fingered her wrist, absently, then frowned. For some inexplicable reason she had decided to wear her bracelet, Andreas's wedding present to her. It was on the dressing-table; she must remember to get it. A bird swooped into the valley and she watched it, her mind naturally filled with recent dramatic events.

'Just for one night you'll be all my own. I know you'll hate me,' her husband had said, in tones edged with sadness, and she fully expected to discover the truth of those last words of his. But did she hate him? All her confusion returned as she recalled again her doubts, her bewilderment whenever her husband's image intruded into her mind.

He came towards her and she turned, wondering that he could look the same, his face so set and stern, his eyes cold and hard as steel. What did she herself look like? She had combed her hair without even glancing in a mirror. She knew her face was flushed, her eyes bright with a new awareness. She also knew that the heart that should have been cold with hate was beating far too quickly, creating a warmth that suffused her whole body. Her husband regarded her for a moment, taking in her heightened colour and the nervous little movement of her hands. But he made no comment on these things as he said, in tones of faint admonition,

'I expected my breakfast to be on the table when I came from the bathroom. Instead, I find you standing on the terrace here, dreaming.' No tenderness, just a matter-of-fact tone that might have come from a man married for years.

'I'll get you something.' Faintly embarrassed, she lowered her head as she passed close by him. 'Do you want a cooked breakfast? I saw bacon and eggs in the fridge.'

He shook his head.

'Not for me; just coffee and toast, with a little marmalade. You have what you want.'

She moved away, amazed that he could be so impersonal and aloof. He acted as though she was nothing more to him than any casual acquaintance.

They ate the meal on the terrace, even though clouds masked the sun, stealing its warmth. No words were spoken and Shani wondered what her husband was thinking. Was he convinced of her hate? – believing the truth of his own bitter words? Should she tell him of her bewilderment? Should she own that the hatred she had felt for him had been slowly dissolving, and that now it had almost disappeared?

How could she, knowing he did not love her?

And yet on the way back to the hospital she did try

to open a conversation so that she could tell him of her feelings, but each time he responded in monosyllables and at last she fell silent, deciding a more favourable opportunity would later present itself.

On their arrival at Loutras he was immediately told he was required at the hospital in Nicosia. He explained to Matron about running out of petrol and being stranded on the mountain.

'We put up at an hotel,' was all the information he gave, and the next moment he was gone. Shani later learned that he had gone from Nicosia to Athens, where he would stay for two or three weeks, completing the holidays due to him.

The following evening Shani tried to ring Brian, but he was on duty; she tried again on Thursday evening, with the same result. Would he be up at the weekend? she wondered. She hoped so. The sooner her confession was made the better. About this she now had few qualms. The light had been dawning since Brian's unkindness on the occasion of her telling him about her marriage. Gradually since then she had come to realize that life with him would not be the smooth path of bliss she had at first envisaged. Perhaps she was too idealistic, perhaps disillusionment would be hers whichever way she shaped her life. What was to come would come ... but at least she could start right. Her thoughts switched automatically to Andreas, and to her own surprising reaction to his planned victory over her. Hatred and vowed unforgiveness should have been her all-consuming emotions; instead she had found herself enveloped in a new wonderment, for although Andreas did not love her he had proved to be a gentle lover whose tenderness had come as a complete surprise to

Shani, steeling herself as she had for the embraces of a man unbridled and lacking in finesse. Surely she thought, he could not win her by lovemaking alone? This was no basis on which to build a lasting marriage— Staggered by her contemplations, Shani tried to forget that night and get back to the realms of sound common sense, putting from her any idea of making her life with that dark foreigner who even now was little more than a stranger. . . . She shook her head. How could he be a stranger to her when he was her husband in every sense of the word?

Brian came on the Friday evening, ringing her from Nicosia, saying he would meet her at the *taverna* which they both favoured, not only because of its position near the sea, but also because it was surrounded by palm trees and pines, giving it a sort of romantic seclusion. Hardly the place in which to impart her news, decided Shani as she chose a table outside the café. Soon Brian drove on to the car park, sending up a cloud of dust that settled on the snow-white tablecloth. Although perplexed by his air of triumph and the definite swagger with which he approached the table Shani was totally unprepared for the information she was shortly to receive.

He wasted no time but, sitting down opposite to her, he said in ringing tones,

'I've settled him! Did Manou mention anything to you about my phone call?'

'Phone call?' A trembling hand fluttered to Shani's cheek. 'You rang Andreas? What about?'

'The annulment! I saw a lawyer at the base and he said it was right that your husband was the injured party – or would be considered so. I therefore decided to treat him to a dose of his own medicine. I told him that if he didn't annul the marriage in quick time I'd expose him – tell the world what he'd done to you! How about that, my love? Proud of your clever young man?' His handsome face was flushed with satisfaction. All Shani could do was stare, aghast.

'You actually held a gun at my – at Andreas's head?' she quivered at last.

'He held one at yours, all those years ago, so why not?' He laughed at her expression, misreading it. 'A marvellous idea – came to me all of a sudden! And it was damned effective, I can tell you; he never so much as argued. Just accepted it.' He laughed again, jeeringly, and Shani winced. How could she ever have loved this man? – contemplated spending the rest of her life with him? 'I don't anticipate any trouble from your husband, my sweet. Everything's going to be plain sailing from now on.' He reached for her hand, but she moved it from the table. Brian frowned at her action, but said cheerfully, 'We'll be married in no time at all – now that I've taken a hand in the affair. Your husband-in-name-only is utterly defeated!'

His words registered, but vaguely. Her thoughts were elsewhere. Threats, Andreas had mentioned. Threats that he had dealt with in his own effective way.

'When did you ring Andreas?' she asked, wondering if she were as pale as she felt.

'On Tuesday morning. I'd seen the lawyer soon after I phoned you on Monday evening, but I couldn't then get through to your husband, even though I tried several times. So I got him on Tuesday morning and successfully said my little piece!'

Successfully. . . . Shani could have laughed. She said in a cracked and high-pitched voice that brought her companion's head up with a jerk,

'So he was defeated, was he?'

'Absolutely. Never said a word!'

'Not one word?'

He shrugged, and amended his statement.

'He did slip in a word or two now and then.'

'Agreeing to annul the marriage?' Shani threw him a sideways glance.

'Not verbally, but, as I've said, he was utterly defeated.' Brian paused a moment. 'Just before I rang off he did try a little bluff—'

'Bluff?'

'It was when I told him he was beaten, and so he'd better give in with good grace—'

'You said that to Andreas!'

'Of course. And then he said he was beaten only when a situation was out of his control – and that this was certainly not out of his control. It was bluff, obviously,' ended Brian with a sneer.

'Was my name mentioned?' she inquired curiously, wondering why Andreas had kept silent about the telephone conversation with Brian. 'Apart from when you threatened him, I mean?'

'He asked if you were aware that I intended threatening him. I said you knew nothing about this telephone call but that you would fully approve of my action. I told him you didn't care what method we used so long as we made him free you.'

'In other words he – he believed I was a party to – to what you were doing?' She felt quite faint. Andreas was believing that of her – on the night of his tender lovemaking. And he still believed it of her, believed she had told Brian she did not care what methods were used so long as he was made to free her.

'I said you were quite determined to marry me—Yes, he believed you were a party to what I was doing.' The waiter appeared and Brian took up the menu. 'Come, sweetheart, let's have a bumper feast – a second celebration!'

Food. . . . She said unemotionally,

'There's nothing to celebrate.'

He knit his brows, becoming aware at last of her pallor.

'What do you mean?' he asked uneasily.

'Just what I say. There's nothing to celebrate.'

Brian waved the waiter away and came forward in his chair, regarding her searchingly.

'You'd better explain.'

She met his gaze and found no real anxiety there, just a slight uncertainty, nothing more. In fact, a glint of triumph remained, and on his mouth was the sneer displayed when he had spoken so disparagingly of her husband.

'Your interference,' she said in icy tones, 'led Andreas to take the law into his own hands – to make impossible the obtaining of an annulment.' A fleeting hesitation before she added, 'He made me stay the night with him at a villa he has in the mountains.' No blushes, no stammering. Just an unemotional statement that wiped the triumph from Brian's eyes and the sneer from his mouth.

'You – he?' A purple tinge crept under Brian's skin. 'I don't believe it!'

'It would be rather pointless for me to lie about a

matter such as this.'

Black fury leapt to his eyes.

'The fiend!' People at a nearby table glanced across, but he was blind to their interest. 'You had to stay there – to endure – ? My God, but he'll pay for this! I'll have his name dragged in the mire—'

'Just a moment, Brian.' Shani was white to the lips and her heart raced madly, but she did manage to keep her voice controlled as she went on to explain the change that had been taking place in her feelings for Brian.

'I had made up my mind, before – before Andreas and I spent the night at the villa, that I would tell you this weekend when you came up,' she went on. 'That's what I meant when I said there was more to it than Andreas's adamant attitude regarding the annulment. I could have told you over the phone, and as things have turned out I certainly wish I had, but how was I to know you'd take it upon yourself to interfere in that way?'

'Interfere? I had every right to interfere, I was your future husband!'

But Shani shook her head.

'I've just told you, Brian, that my feelings for you had already undergone a change.'

He stared at her, veins throbbing in his neck.

'You sit there, calmly telling me that! And the other,' he said between his teeth, 'that doesn't appear to be troubling you overmuch. Anyone would think you enjoyed it!'

At that the colour rushed to her face. Her legs felt weak, but she managed to rise from her chair.

'I hadn't meant us to part enemies,' she said gently,

'but it seems we are doing. You had no right whatsoever to threaten my husband – and if you knew him as well as I you wouldn't lightly have passed off his comment as bluff; you'd have been greatly perturbed by it. What he did hasn't come as a surprise to me, not now that I know the circumstances. Andreas is too strong a man to be browbeaten by anyone.' She picked up her handbag from a chair, fingering it a trifle agitatedly. 'Brian . . . you won't mention this to anyone? Please don't let it be known that Andreas is my husband.' He said nothing and she added pleadingly, 'You won't talk – promise?'

'You need have no fear,' he snarled at last, his eyes roving over her. 'I shan't mention either of you as long as I live!'

'Thank you.' She stood there, watching the convulsive movement of his hand as he clenched and unclenched it, gripping the tablecloth at times in this display of fury. 'I'm sorry—'

'Don't waste your breath on apologies. I wouldn't have you now – and I don't suppose anyone else will, either,' he added contemptuously.

'My husband will,' she returned gently, and left him.

CHAPTER SEVEN

WITH the utterance of that statement, so confident and firm, the blockage of doubt was removed and Shani knew it was her husband she wanted. She also knew that the idea of living with him had been forming in her mind for some time, and that it had been strengthened by those idyllic days on Cos.

A week had gone by since her last meeting with Brian, and almost a fortnight had passed since Andreas went away. There had been no communication, but then she had not expected him to write. Gossip and speculation could only result from the arrival at the hospital of a letter from Mr. Manou to Sister Reeves. But for the entire period of his absence Shani's mind had been absorbed by the prospect of making her life with him. At times she would be depressed by the knowledge that he did not love her, yet despite the firm conviction that marriage should be based on foundations far stronger than her husband was able to supply he now drew her irresistibly and she desired only to be with him. Immediately he returned she would go to him; he would learn that, far from hating him as he believed, she was on the contrary feeling very differently about him. He'd be so glad to have her — perhaps he would even learn to love her in time, she thought, conscious of a glow within her at the possibility of this.

Just over a fortnight had elapsed when she began to suspect that, had she still been undecided about her future, the matter might have been taken out of her hands. With the passing of another week she felt almost certain of this.

'When is Mr. Manou coming back?' she inquired breathlessly of Matron. She felt so excited she could scarcely contain her impatience. Would he be glad? But of course he would!

'On Wednesday.' Matron looked critically at her. 'You appear to be very happy, Sister. Have you won the National Lottery, or something?'

Shani laughed.

'No, it's nothing like that.' The words were out before she realized they must inevitably prompt another question.

'What is it, then? – or mustn't I ask?'

'I can't tell you about it yet,' she apologized, and Matron did not press her. They talked for a while and then Shani went to her room. She was off duty for the day, but had promised to visit Luciana, a young Greek Cypriot girl who had recently been a patient at the hospital. Luciana lived with her mother in a pretty blue and white house in the village. She worked in an office in Nicosia, staying with her married sister during the week and coming home to her mother at the week-ends. Now, however, she was convalescing and had invited Shani to come and meet her mother.

Although outwardly attractive, the house was scant-ily equipped with furnishings. This was the case with most homes of the poorer classes. Working hours as well as leisure were spent out of doors, and so long as there were adequate beds and a table and some chairs no embellishments were considered necessary. The wealthier classes, most of whom had visited England or

America, often went to the other extreme and Shani had been into houses where she actually felt smothered by comfort.

'Have some refreshment,' invited Luciana when, the introduction having been made, Luciana's mother returned to her work in the kitchen garden at the back of the house. 'I've made the drink from pomegranates. I'm sure you'll enjoy it very much.'

'I know I will; I've had it before.' Shani was on the patio, staring out towards the mountains. Wednesday ... the day after tomorrow. So odd that she experienced such eagerness after the way she had fled in terror from her husband.

'You'll eat also?' Luciana reappeared from the house carrying a tray on which was a small *mezé* consisting of meat and fish, of tomatoes and cheese, and the tasty young *anguri* – the small cucumbers that were served with everything. The *mezé* had obviously been prepared beforehand and although Shani was not hungry, having lunched only an hour previously, she could not bring herself to hurt Luciana's feelings by ignoring the dishes set out before her. 'Cheese?' The Cypriot girl looked questioningly at her. 'Do you like *haloumi*? – or *phetta*?'

'I'll just help myself,' smiled Shani. 'I'm equally fond of them both.'

It was only when Luciana sat down that Shani noticed she also appeared to be excited about something. She did not have long to wait; Luciana soon began telling her about Antonakis, a young man from Famagusta who had recently offered for her.

'His parents came to see my mother last week,' she went on. 'They wanted to know about my *prika*, and

Mother showed them this house, and told them I have some fields of olives. I have some bananas also and a few oranges. I think it is arranged.'

'This is all yours?' Shani made a comprehensive gesture with her hand.

Luciana nodded.

'This is my dowry house. Father gave it to me before he died.'

'But your mother? Will she live with you?'

'She might live with us, but she might live in the shack.'

Shani's eyes clouded.

'Your father didn't have enough money to build you a house – so he gave you his?' Often this occurred, Shani knew, especially if the man happened to have several daughters.

'He had to.' Luciana grimaced. 'I have four sisters.' She pointed to the house just up the lane. 'Mr. Spiros and his wife had to give their house to their daughter, and now they live in that tiny place at the side.'

'It's so different from England,' said Shani musingly. 'Here, the young couple start life with a house and furniture, and enough land to provide them with a living. They often end up in a much inferior house, or, as you say, in a shack. In my country the couple start with very little and end up comfortably off and living in a house far superior to that in which they began. At least, that's the general picture.'

A wistful expression settled on Luciana's face.

'In England it is a good way. You fall in love, don't you? I watch your films on television and it seems a very nice thing to fall in love. You choose your own husbands, don't you?'

About to agree, Shani stopped, wondering what Luciana would say were she to know that Shani had been 'offered' for and constrained into marriage with a man she had not loved.

'This Antonakis,' she said at length. 'What's he like?'

'I've never seen him.'

'Never—!' Shani stared uncomprehendingly. Couples here had no preliminary courtship before marriage, but normally they were acquainted, or at least knew one another by sight. 'He's seen you, obviously?'

'Just once. He came to call on his friend, Yannis, who works in my office. I did not notice Antonakis because so many people come into the office, but Antonakis noticed me and asked Yannis about me. Yannis told him I was a good girl and did not walk with boys. So Antonakis asked his parents to come and see my mother.'

'You're happy at the thought of marrying him?'

'I – think so, yes.' Luciana quickly dropped her eyes to the dishes so daintily laid out on the table. 'You are not eating, Sister Reeves.'

'Thank you.' Shani took a small piece of *phetta* and began nibbling it. She felt anxious about the girl and said hesitantly, 'You're quite sure you're happy, Luciana?'

Sudden doubt entered the dark eyes, and then, with a sigh of resignation Luciana said quietly,

'I am happy, Sister Reeves.'

'But supposing, when you meet this boy, you don't like him?'

'I asked Yannis about him and he said he is a nice

boy and that he is kind to his sisters.'

Shani changed the subject because to her it was de
pressing. Luciana was so young, and so sensitive. Sh
should be courted and petted a little, and led into th
unpredictable state of marriage by gentle persuasiv
steps. Instead, her aspiring husband calculatingly sen
his parents to assess her store of worldly goods. On th
value of these alone would be based his decision
whether or not to marry the girl.

'When are you returning to work, Luciana?'

'Next week. I'm feeling much better and could
have gone this week, but when I visited the hospital on
Friday Dr. Gordon told me to have another week a
home. I don't like to do this because we have only a
small allowance when we're off work.' She looked a
Shani. 'I don't get much money when I do work
though, so it's perhaps better that I get married—' She
broke off as an old man opened the gate and ambled
into the garden.

'*Yassoo!*'

'*Yassoo,*' returned the girls in unison. 'I'm glad
you've come,' added Luciana. 'Mr. Spiros's goats have
been on my land.' She stood up. 'Sister Reeves, do you
know Mr. George, the Guardian of the Fields?'

Shani nodded, taking the proffered hand.

'George's wife was in the hospital some weeks
ago.'

'Of course. I forgot. Mr. George, will you have a
glass of wine, or do you wish for *ouzo*?'

'My usual – *ouzo*, if you please, Luciana.' He took
possession of a chair and Luciana went into the house
to fetch the drink.

'I pay you ten shillings a year to see that my neighbours don't allow their animals to stray on to my fields,' she said severely on handing him his glass. 'You are not doing your job, Mr. George.'

'You didn't report it, and I heard about it only this day. I shall go in a few minutes to Mr. Spiros and tell him to keep his goats tethered.' He looked at Shani and gave a little shrug. 'The goats did not do any harm at all.'

'That's not the point. They could have done some damage if I hadn't seen them. I was very cross with Mr. Spiros.' She sat down, looking very small and fragile. Shani could not imagine her being cross with anyone. 'I hope you will also give him a good telling off.'

'He pays me ten shillings a year as well as you!'

'And because of that,' came the swift retort, 'he would be angry if my goats strayed on to his fields.'

'Ten shillings a year is not much,' protested George, 'not for all I do—' He stopped as Luciana's eyes opened wide.

'Not much! Mr. George, there are two thousand of us paying you that sum. You must be very rich!'

'That's nothing to do with it. *You* pay me only ten shillings and look what I do for it. I guard your fields—'

'No, you don't. What about Mr. Spiros's goats?'

'I guard your fields,' repeated George, ignoring the interruption. 'I keep the peace in the village—'

'The peace? Those children of Maroula's are always making a noise. Every day when Loukis goes to school he kicks a can all along the lane. Then he kicks it back again on the way home. My mother is deafened by it!'

'I'll speak with Maroula.'

'And you didn't turn my water on last Saturday. My oranges won't be ready.'

He wagged a finger at her.

'You have it on Mondays and Thursdays, and that's all you're entitled to. Why should you expect to have it every day?'

'I don't, but I asked you to change the days, because I want water on Saturdays.'

'What difference does it make?'

'I'm at home on Saturdays, so I can see to the trenches. If I'm not there the water runs away.'

'Your mother can do the trenches.' George picked up a piece of meat and put it in his mouth, at the same time throwing an exasperated glance in Luciana's direction. 'She has plenty of time.'

'My mother has no time. The garden is hard work, you know that, Mr. George, with the ground getting baked every day as it does, and having to be broken up all the time with that heavy axe.'

This interchange eventually brought a laugh from Shani, but so engrossed were the other two that neither spared her even a glance.

The water arrangements were made many years ago, said George, and they could not be changed. Luciana's ancestor had bought the rights from the ancestor of the man who now owned the spring, and Luciana was entitled to have the water for two hours on Mondays and three hours on Thursdays, and as far as George was concerned this must go on for ever.

'But why? Mr. Savvas doesn't mind changing days with me.'

George shook his head emphatically.

'The rules, Luciana. We must keep to the rules.'

'Don't you think they're silly?' Luciana turned to Shani at last, spreading her hands in a gesture of frustration.

'Well, yes, I do, seeing that Savvas doesn't mind. But I also know how inflexible the rules are on the island. Can't you prepare the trenches beforehand?'

'It isn't the preparing of them, it's the blocking off when a tree has had enough water, and then directing the water to another tree.' She shook her head. 'No, someone must be there when the trees are being watered, otherwise it goes all over the place – just runs to waste.'

'Couldn't you store some of this water?' suggested Shani, trying to be helpful.

'She can,' interposed George, 'but only outside. It's not permitted to pipe it into the house. That was never in the agreement.'

'I know it's not permitted to pipe it, but surely there's nothing to stop Luciana storing it in tanks?'

'I don't want to store it in tanks. I want to have it flowing easily on to my land. When I'm married, Mr. George, you'll have to do what my husband tells you, or he won't pay you – and then where would you be?'

Another laugh broke from Shani on seeing the effect of those words on George. He seemed about to have a fit; he also seemed quite prepared to continue the argument indefinitely and after thanking Luciana for her hospitality Shani made her departure, unheeded by either of the others as they were now both speaking at once.

At last Andreas arrived back at Loutras and although she knew the correct procedure would be to find out if he was free to see her – or better still to call at his house later in the day – Shani succumbed to her eagerness and decided to contact him right away. Before anything else there must come an apology for Brian's behaviour, she decided, and also a declaration that she herself had not approved of it. Reaching Andreas's room, she omitted to knock, and as she opened the door it was to see a dark frown suddenly cross his face.

'Kindly knock before you enter,' he snapped, and for a moment Shani could only gasp and stare.

'Knock?'

'Isn't it usual to knock before entering a doctor's room?' His brows were raised, his regard arrogant. He was her superior; she was merely Sister Reeves and not his wife at all. This staggering change! Had three weeks away erased the memory of both the holiday and that night spent in his villa up in the pine forest of Troodos? But his baffling manner was soon explained as it dawned on Shani that while to her their future was settled, to him the position was no different from the one existing on the morning they came down from Troodos. He was not to know how she felt or why she had come. On the contrary, he believed she hated him and still loved Brian. Moreover, he believed she approved of Brian's action because Brian had told him so. With these things in mind she said gently,

'I want to talk to you, Andreas,' but then she stopped, glancing round. It were better to have waited. The clinical atmosphere of a hospital was not the setting for what she had to say. 'I'll come to your house this evening,' she began eagerly, when he interrupted her.

'I'm going out this evening.' His voice was hard; he neither looked at her nor offered her a chair. 'Whatever you have to say can be said here.' Shani's eyes dropped to his hand, clenched tightly as it lay on the desk. He seemed on the defensive ... yet ready to attack.

'I don't want to speak here,' she began, quite deflated, and unable to remember any of the eloquent phrases she had so happily rehearsed. 'It's about – us – and our marriage. If you'll tell me when you are free? I would much prefer to come to your house. There is so much to say.'

'There can't be much to say. It's all been said. I'm not listening to your recriminations, or your declarations that you now intend to seek for a divorce. The marriage could until recently have been dissolved by me alone; now it can be dissolved by neither of us. From the first I've desired only that you give the marriage a trial, which you refused to do – even on the holiday, when I thought that perhaps we had come close. I expect you're still seeing this Brian, whom you know by now had the audacity to offer me an ultimatum, an act which, he said, you would fully approve. That,' he added bitterly, 'shocked me. Somehow I would have expected you to deplore a threat such as that. However, I took my own action, deliberately keeping silent about the threat in order not to arouse your suspicions. I make no excuses; my conscience is clear because I acted according to my beliefs – and those are that marriage is a permanent state.'

No anger in his voice, nothing to terrify her as on

various other occasions . . . and yet she was terrified, even before he continued, telling her that he was now no longer interested in her or the idea of making their lives together. He had other plans, and from now on she need have no fear that he would intrude into her life or question her actions. He paused, his eyes dark and bitter. Shani tried to speak . . . but what price all her plans now? He was no longer interested in her.

'When I leave here in six months' time our paths will divide and I don't suppose we shall ever meet again. I sincerely hope we don't,' he added, and if Shani had clung to any shred of hope it deserted her now. For there was no doubt at all about the sincerity of those words. They were uttered with feeling and strength; he had never been more serious about anything in his life. 'As for our respective positions in the hospital,' he went on, once more assuming the cool dispassionate manner of her superior, 'we must remember them. I hope I won't have to remind you again about this.' His attention was arrested and Shani turned automatically to follow the direction of his gaze. Lydia was crossing the grounds, making for the tree-shaded enclosure in which stood Andreas's house. She entered the pathway, closing the gate behind her, and then she disappeared into the house. Shani cast a swift glance at Andreas; the hardness had disappeared from his face as, rising, he made for the door. It was held open for Shani to pass through in front of him. Neither spoke a word as with the closing of the door they went their separate ways.

The window on the corridor looked out on to the lawn at the side of the hospital. Andreas was crossing it, proceeding towards his house.

Two days later there was the ordeal of working with Andreas in the theatre.

'You look pale,' he remarked after giving her his customary nod and brief 'Good morning, Sister'. 'Are you not feeling well?'

'I'm quite all right, thank you, sir.'

Andreas threw her another cursory glance and then gave his whole attention to the task in hand.

Jenny also remarked on Shani's loss of colour and on the day they were to attend the village wedding she said anxiously,

'Are you all right, Shani? You don't look at all well.'

Shani gave a little sigh. It was to be hoped she wasn't going to continue like this, otherwise she would have to leave sooner than she intended.

'I've a headache,' she said by way of an excuse, but added, 'I'm going to the wedding, though. I promised Elpidha, and so I must.'

Elpidha's small brother had recently been a patient at Loutras and this was a good excuse for inviting the entire staff to the wedding. During her visits to see her brother Elpidha had become particularly attached to Andreas, and also to Shani, and their invitations had been delivered by the girl herself, who had begged them to attend, if it were at all possible.

Both being off duty, Shani and Jenny ordered a taxi and went together, arriving at the village of Ayios Vasilios in time for some of the pre-wedding festivities and rites. The *koumbari* – or best men – were dancing with the mattress outside the bride's house. The maidens then decorated it, sewing into the four corners red

135

crosses. Incredibly the couple wanted a girl for their first child, and a two-year-old girl was rolled on the mattress. Money was then thrown upon it, the bride's mother appeared with the incense, and after all the bride's trousseau and other beautifully-embroidered linen was piled upon it the mattress was rolled up and carried by the bride's father, on his shoulder, to the couple's new house. Dancing and singing went on all the time; in the mud ovens hundreds of loaves were being baked, on the spits chickens and meat and tiny pigs were being cooked over the smoking charcoal, while inside the house the bride's maidens were preparing her for the ceremony. The priest was in attendance all the time and he it was who shaved the bridegroom in readiness for the wedding. In the bride's lemon orchard long tables were set out, covered with gleaming white cloths. The whole village was on holiday, for Cypriot weddings were always held on Sundays. At last the procession wound its way up to the church, the little girl attendants carrying lighted, beribboned candles almost as tall as themselves. The church was entered, with everyone talking at once. Never had Shani heard such a babble of voices.

'These weddings really are a hoot!' Jenny nudged her friend and pointed to a youth who was getting out his camera. In Greek he requested the bearded priest to halt the service while he took a snapshot. The priest smilingly obliged and the couple turned, all three posing for the shot. No sooner had the ceremony recommenced than the same thing happened again, and this went on the whole time. Meanwhile, the best men were passing round a long length of ribbon, on which they each wrote their name. 'The best men pay for everything, did you know that?'

Shani nodded, her thoughts going involuntarily to her own wedding, with the congregation so reverent and the priest so serious. Here, there was so much laughing and talking that Shani felt doubtful of anyone's hearing a word of the service.

There must be a thousand guests, she calculated on coming out of the church. There was dancing and singing, eating and drinking, and this went on for hours. Tomorrow there would be a repetition, and the following day there would be a special party for the best men and the bride's maidens.

The bride and groom took no part in the festivities, merely sitting in the house and handing out wedding biscuits to each guest in turn. Later, however, the bride came out and performed her ceremonial dance, and there followed the custom of pinning money on to her dress. Soon it was covered with notes and her husband joined her, his clothes also being covered with notes.

'All that money!' exclaimed Jenny. 'They can collect as much as five hundred pounds in this way. They say all this is fast disappearing, but I'll bet that's one custom that will survive!'

'Did you see all the presents?'

'Stacked right up to the ceiling. I just tossed mine among them — felt I needn't have bothered, for I'm sure they'll never know who's brought what.'

'I think Elpidha will go through all the cards. She seems to be a rather sentimental little girl.'

'Perhaps you're right,' agreed Jenny, holding out her glass for more champagne. 'She is sweet. Do you suppose it's a love match?'

'Could be. Costa was approached by the parents of a

much wealthier girl, but he chose Elpidha.'

'Good for him. He's rather nice, too – and he works!'

It was not until Shani was pinning on her money that she noticed her husband. He was with Lydia and they also were among the last to pin on their offerings. Shani and Jenny had each pinned on a one-pound note and then stepped back.

'Did you see what Lydia gave?' whispered Jenny. 'A fiver! That's only because Mr. Manou gave that sum,' she added disparagingly.

Lydia turned, gave Shani a condescending look before saying to her companion,

'Andreas, shall we go now? We're dining with the Benson-Smythes, remember.'

'Benson-Smythes,' scoffed Jenny. 'I'll bet their name was plain Smith back in England!'

Shani laughed.

'I believe they're quite nice people,' she returned musingly. 'I should imagine they must be, for I'm sure Mr. Manou would be most selective in his choice of friends.'

'You are?' Jenny's eyes followed the couple as they went towards Andreas's car. 'Then how do you account for his interest in that one?'

Shani couldn't and so she said nothing, but merely watched as they got into the car. A few moments later it edged its way through the laughing throng and was lost to sight round a bend in the road.

CHAPTER EIGHT

The first time Shani fainted she was alone; the second time she was in Matron's room. She had been on her way out to do some shopping and had stopped to give Matron a message. When she came to Dr. Gordon was holding her wrist.

'Have you any idea why you fainted, Sister?' he asked.

She hesitated. Had they guessed? She felt sure they had, but in any case she couldn't have lied. A small silence followed her admission and then Matron spoke.

'Brian knows, of course?' her voice was pained and tinged with regret.

'No.' The doctor moved away and Shani clasped her hands in her lap. 'Brian and I haven't been going out together for some time.'

'So I believe.' The doctor spoke quietly and without the least hint of censure. 'Jenny mentioned that you had parted.'

'We haven't seen each other for six weeks.' She played for time, unable to collect her thoughts or decide what to say.

Matron looked gravely at her.

'You're going to tell him, surely?'

She shook her head, and a long, trembling sigh left her lips.

'It – it isn't Brian's child,' she managed to say after a long hesitation. Never had she thought to feel so ashamed and embarrassed as this, and for a moment she knew a return of her old hatred against Andreas.

'Not Brian's? Then whose . . .?' Matron spoke reflectively and Shani caught her breath. Could she possibly have made a guess at the truth? Shani wasn't left long in doubt; eager to escape, she declared she was feeling better and left the room, only to turn back as she remembered her shopping bag, lying by the desk where she had dropped it as she fell.

'I have my suspicions,' Matron was saying, 'though I dare not voice them. But I've just recalled a little scene here when Sister was looking particularly happy. When I asked the reason for this she said she could not tell me yet. Obviously she was expecting the man to marry her, and obviously he's refused.'

'You can't voice your suspicions, you say? Is he one of the staff?'

'I can't say anything, Doctor. But I'm almost certain I know who the father is.'

A hand fluttered to Shani's cheek. Matron was acute – but that little scene as she called it could not in itself give rise to her suspicions. Matron was also remembering that Shani and Mr. Manou had been 'stranded' on Troodos, and forced to stay there – at an hotel, Andreas had said.

At last Shani knocked and pushed open the door.

'I left my bag.' Picking it up, she looked at Matron. 'You won't say anything?' Her face was white; she felt ready to faint again.

'Naturally this will go no further,' was the pointed reply, but then Matron added, 'When you're feeling up to it perhaps you'd like to come and discuss your plans with me?'

'I'd like to stay on for a while,' she began, when the doctor interrupted her.

'Have a rest now, and then do what Matron suggests. Come and have a talk with her.'

A few minutes later Shani was lying on her bed, staring up at the ceiling and thinking of the high esteem in which Matron had always held her. A tear escaped and she could almost have gone down and blurted out the truth, astounding them both by saying yes, it was Andreas's child, but they need not feel sorry for her because she was legally married. However, the temptation soon died. It was by her own choosing that she had discarded her wedding ring and posed as a single woman. Had she known her own mind just a little sooner everything would have been all right, but now Andreas's interest in her had been lost and he no longer wished to acknowledge her as his wife. She had no right to expose him to gossip which must assuredly discredit him. There was one consolation: once away from Loutras she would assume her married name and be saved any further humiliation. Already she had been making plans, though only in her mind as yet. Her father had left her money which fortunately she had not touched. With Matron's agreement she would remain at Loutras for another month or two and then leave for England where she would make her home with her aunt until the baby was born. Then, if her aunt was unwilling to have the trouble of a child in the house, Shani would find herself a small place and later, with her child at school, she would take a part-time nursing post at one of the local hospitals. That was as far as her plans went. She wanted the child and considered it to be her very own. Should Andreas learn of its existence he would most certainly demand that it live with him for part of the time; determined that her child would be brought up in a stable environment, she made the firm decision not to let her husband know anything about it.

She saw Matron the next day and told her of the plans she had made.

'Your aunt will have you?' Matron asked anxiously after Shani had admitted that she had not yet written to her.

'I'm sure she will. I'm her only niece and she'll be glad to have me live with her.'

'Well, that sounds a satisfactory enough arrangement.' Matron paused a moment, looking straight at Shani. 'About staying here,' she went on doubtfully and, Shani was quick to notice, with a touch of caution, 'do you really consider it wise?'

No mistaking the subtle advice, and Shani flushed. And yet her thoughts were not at the moment concerned with her own embarrassment. She was wondering what Matron was thinking of Andreas. Her inevitable condemnation of him, resulting from the belief that he had acted unprofessionally, troubled Shani, but there was nothing she could do about it. In any case, his reputation was safe enough. Matron had said herself she dared not voice her suspicions and this was true – for the simple reason that although she was convinced that Andreas was the father of Shani's child, she could not be absolutely sure of this.

Shani fell to wondering what would happen were the truth to come out at any time. Andreas would then have to reveal the fact of his marriage in order to keep his good name.

'I'd like to stay,' Shani said at last. 'The money will come in useful.' Which was true, because if she did have to find her own place her money would have to be stretched. Nevertheless, Shani knew the money was not the important factor. While she remained at Loutras there was the remote possibility of a reconciliation; once she left the break would be final. And yet Shani knew she clung to an extremely weak thread of hope, for hadn't Andreas made absolutely clear his loss of interest in her? Hadn't he said with truth that when their ways divided he never wanted to set eyes on her again?

'I suppose the money is important,' agreed Matron. 'But have you thought of the possibility of your fainting in the theatre?' It would be unbearably embarrassing both for Shani and the surgeon, Matron was concluding, sure as she was that Andreas knew of Shani's condition.

'I'm hoping I'll soon be past the fainting stage,' said Shani with a slight smile. 'After all, it's only a phase, and doesn't normally last long.'

Matron shrugged.

'How long do you want to remain here?'

'About two months.'

After some consideration Matron agreed, but, strangely, Shani left the room with mixed feelings. Perhaps it were better to make the break now. What hope did she really have? Andreas's interest in her had waned ... or been transferred perhaps to Lydia Murray. It was inviting heartache to stay. Too late she had discovered her feelings for her husband ... just a little too late.

Shani did not faint in the theatre, but sometimes she

would feel off-colour and on one occasion, after Andreas had searched her face critically for a long moment, he said,

'You're pale, Sister. Are you not well?'

Shani's heart gave a jerk. Would he want her if he knew? Undoubtedly – but what satisfaction could she derive from the knowledge that she was accepted merely for the sake of the child? With her own new and tender emotions strong within her she was not prepared to make her life with Andreas unless he had at least some interest in his wife for herself.

'I'm perfectly well, sir.' Her voice was deliberately cold and unemotional, because she feared he might guess her secret. The child was hers, she thought fiercely, possessively. If Andreas knew about it he would want to share it, even though Shani refused to live with him.

Andreas turned away, taking his gloves from Chrystalla. And as he drew them on he seemed to sigh inwardly. Perhaps, thought Shani, he was feeling very fatigued. Yesterday he had performed two major operations in Nicosia, and the one he was about to begin would be his second for today.

'He seems to be always in a foul mood these days,' said Jenny a week later as she came off duty, having done the ward round with him. 'I'll be jolly glad when he's gone!'

'He was in a temper, you mean?' They were on Shani's verandah, drinking coffee.

'Not exactly – but just in an aggravating mood. He asked Mrs. Ronson if she was getting enough to eat and she said no. He considered it was all my fault.'

'Mrs. Ronson never has enough to eat. She has an

appetite like a horse.'

'I know, and so does everyone else – except Mr. Manou.'

'Didn't you tell him she's always grumbling?'

'And get my head snapped off? Not likely! He was bad enough when he first came, but now he's unbearable.' Shani said nothing and after a while Jenny said musingly, 'I wonder what he's like with Lydia? She seems glowing enough these days, so I expect he keeps a special front just for her alone.'

Shani poured more coffee, a frown creasing her brow. How could she ever have wished he would fall in love with Lydia? And yet she had wished it, just so that he would agree to an annulment.

'I'm leaving soon, Jenny,' she said quietly at last, changing the subject. 'I want to go back to England,' she added hastily as Jenny gasped and opened her mouth to question her. 'As you know, my aunt's all alone . . .'

'Your aunt? But you've never troubled yourself about her before; you said she liked living alone.' Jenny looked at her curiously. 'You've always said you loved the island, would be sad at leaving.'

An awkward silence followed. Shani had known how difficult it would be to inform her friend she was leaving, and for that reason she had kept putting it off.

'I just want to leave, Jen. Please don't ask me any questions.'

'Brian?' queried Jenny, ignoring her pleas. 'You're very upset about the break?'

'It was rather upsetting,' came the evasive reply. Perhaps this was the best way out. Let them all think she was going right away because of Brian. She could think of no other excuse, and an excuse would certainly be expected. It was a weak excuse, and would give the impression of instability in Shani's nature, but it would suffice.

'In my opinion it's a pity you ever met him,' returned her friend bluntly. 'He's a flirt and I don't believe he would ever change his ways.' She paused, but as Shani remained silent she went on, 'You haven't explained a thing about it – never said how it happened?'

'There was a very good reason, Jen, but it's something I just can't talk about, even to you.'

An impatient little shrug and then,

'I'm sorry. I wish I could help.'

'No one can help.' The words came swiftly, involuntarily, and Jenny's face clouded.

'You've definitely made up your mind to leave?'

'Matron knows, and is already negotiating for a replacement.'

'So there's no possibility of your changing your mind?'

Shani shook her head.

'None whatever.' If only she could confide! It would surely help to relieve the weight of misery and hopelessness that was gradually settling on her as with the passing of each day Andreas continued to treat her with almost frigid indifference. But a confidence was impossible and she said dully, 'I'll be home for Christmas.'

'You're leaving so soon? That's in less than six weeks,' added Jenny after a quick calculation.

'It's in five weeks,' returned Shani, having already

begun to count the days.

Jenny picked up her cup, regarding her friend over the rim of it, that curious expression having returned to her eyes. She was puzzled, which was only natural, thought Shani, knowing full well what Jenny was thinking. Shani's strength of character was at complete variance with her decision to throw up her job and leave the island simply because of the break with Brian.

'I suppose you know what you're doing,' said Jenny at length, 'but I'm sure you'll be sorry. I've never yet met anyone who can leave this island without regrets.'

Nor am I leaving without regrets, thought Shani. Bitter regrets at not seeing the light sooner. If only she could go back and re-live those last four days on Cos! If only she had not been filled both with uncertainty and a sense of honour towards Brian. She would have agreed to the honeymoon ... and she would now be with her husband. He had searched for her, and having at last found her he had asked her to live with him—'Think about it, Shani,' he had advised. 'For we've a long way to go and the road can be lonely.' During the holiday he had tried so hard, she saw that now ... and she had refused him. He was now tired of trying; all desire for her was dead and she might just as well abandon hope. Perhaps if he had not given her a demonstration of the intensity of his desire, had not submitted her to those savage kisses of possession, she might the sooner have seen him in a different light. He had come to Cyprus hoping to claim her, clearly not expecting to face the setback of another man having entered her life. The knowledge had inflamed him and his primitive traits had been bared.

Shani had since discovered a very different side to his nature, had known kindness and gentle care when on holiday with him – had later experienced his tenderness as a lover.

The news that she was leaving soon spread, but to her surprise she was not questioned as to the reason. Jenny must have enlightened them and they had practised tact. But there would be gossip; like the rest Andreas would know of her supposed reason for leaving, though he would know there was much more to it than a lovers' quarrel, he himself having made marriage between Shani and Brian impossible. If only she could go to him, and tell him it was nothing to do with Brian – but everything to do with him. He was the only one who never spoke about her going away. He seemed lately to have become sunk in a sort of dull apathy and although he would sometimes nod to Shani in passing, more often he would not notice her at all. In the theatre he rapped out orders and she obeyed. On the wards Jenny – or any other sister who accompanied him – would sigh with relief when the ordeal was over. Only with the patients did he seem to be human, asking about their comfort, and if they had any complaints. And invariably someone suffered the lash of his tongue if a patient did happen to lodge a complaint. Lydia as usual hovered about, being free every afternoon and at the weekends. She was doing clerical work for several of the doctors now, but often she would go over to Andreas's house, sometimes when he himself was busy at the hospital. Comments were made, but no one appeared to be over-curious.

Lydia entered the theatre one afternoon when Shani

was preparing for the operation Andreas would later perform. Under Lydia's arm was a briefcase bearing the stamped initials A.M. and Shani frowned momentarily. Perhaps Lydia was doing work for Andreas also. It was quite feasible, because she seemed to have plenty of time on her hands.

Shani stared questioningly at her visitor, unaware of how lovely she looked in her uniform, her face pale but sweetly composed. She had been engrossed in thoughts of her baby. She wanted a boy, but felt he would be like her, with her colouring. A girl on the other hand would be like Andreas, dark and with fine strong features and sensitive tapering hands. Yes, she decided, she wanted a girl. Andreas would of course have wanted a boy, because all Greek men desired to have a son for their first child. So perhaps she should hope for a boy . . . But a boy would be lost without a father, later on, when he needed companionship. A girl would not miss a father quite so much, so it would be better to wish for— Shani smiled to herself. What good was all this switching of preference? The sex had already been determined.

'I have a message for you.' Lydia came closer to where Shani was checking the instruments.

'Yes?'

'Evynia from the village asked me to tell you your order is ready. You've been having some table mats embroidered, so she says.'

'Thank you for bringing the message. I'll collect them tomorrow.'

'You're leaving us, I hear,' commented Lydia after a pause.

'I am leaving, yes.'

'Before Christmas?'

'That's correct.' Shani left her task and moved away to check the cylinders, hoping Lydia would take the hint, but the girl remained by the table.

'This is all very sudden.'

Shani looked at her, recalling Lydia's confident assertion that she and Andreas would probably announce their engagement on his return from Cos. Lydia had hoped he would take her with him to the island, and that the fortnight's stay together would produce the desired result. He didn't take her and she concluded he had gone alone. What a shock she would receive were she to know he had gone there with his wife!

'There's been a certain amount of speculation as to the reason for your unexpected decision to leave,' remarked Lydia coolly when it became obvious that Shani was not going to speak. 'The staff believe it's owing to a quarrel you've had with your young man.' She moved over to where Shani was once again looking over the trolleys she had earlier set up. The operation was not until four o'clock, Andreas having been operating in Nicosia during the morning and now taking a rest. 'But that's not the real reason, is it, Sister?' The sly note in Lydia's voice, and the phrasing of the question, brought Shani's head up with a jerk.

'I don't think I understand you, Miss Murray?'

A sneering laugh broke, grating on Shani's nerves.

'No one else appears to have noticed, but it's been very clear to me for a while that you've had designs on your boss. Of course, it's nothing new; nurses so often aspire to marry doctors – but they rarely manage to succeed.' She paused a moment and then added, 'I suppose you're finding the situation impossible?'

'Miss Murray,' said Shani in icy tones, 'do you mind

leaving my theatre!'

Lydia's eyes narrowed to mere slits and dark colour fused her cheeks.

'I've already warned you about your lack of respect, Sister. If you're not very careful I'll report you to Matron.'

'Do that by all means, if you consider you have a complaint. Meanwhile, kindly allow me to get on with my work.' Her glance went to the door. Andreas's rest must have been short, because at that moment he walked in. Shani's face was flushed, and so was Lydia's. Andreas glanced from one to the other questioningly. Neither spoke.

'Is anything wrong?' he inquired of Shani.

'No – no, sir.'

'But I'm sure there is. Lydia, why are you here?'

'I came to give Sister Reeves a message,' she smiled, at the same time shaking her head in a gesture of bewilderment. 'Instead of thanking me she ordered me out.'

'Indeed?' His eyes became fixed on Shani, the most odd expression in their depths. 'Is this true, Sister?'

'I did thank her.' For a moment Shani forgot her position, forgot that in the hospital Andreas was her superior. 'She insulted me, and I'm not having her in here! So you can tell her to leave!'

An awful silence followed her words; she put a quivering hand to her mouth but could not bring herself to apologize. Andreas continued to regard her in that peculiar way and although he reprimanded her she had the unaccountable impression that it was merely because he had no choice, Lydia's being a witness to her disrespectful outburst.

Lydia's face was a study of mingled triumph and mystification as she looked from Shani to Andreas who, despite his stern words of censure and warning, was still regarding his wife more with curiosity than with anger.

Shani did not notice either of them. She stared at the floor, her hands clasped in front of her, her face flushed and hot from the lecture she had just received. She was angry with herself, and more angry still with Lydia for goading her into such unmannerly loss of control. And quite illogically she was furious with her husband for coming into the theatre when he wasn't expected. Why, she thought pettishly, wasn't he keeping to routine and taking his rest? He had no right to come into the theatre at this time!

He was waiting for her to look up, intending to speak to her. Sensing this, she deliberately kept her head averted and he spoke to Lydia instead.

'Why did Sister order you out? There must have been some reason for it.'

Lydia shook her head, and shrugged.

'I really don't know, Andreas,' she purred in a forgiving sort of way, and in the manner of one desirous of smoothing over an awkward situation. 'Sister Reeves is probably tired – and a little cross because of it. We all get like that sometimes,' she added, smiling enchantingly up at him. 'Sister was working in here and it's understandable that she should wish to do so without interruption. I do understand that and wouldn't have dreamed of coming here had it not been for the message I was told to pass on to Sister Reeves.' Her lovely eyes were wide open and raised to his; her lips were parted and inviting. Shani glanced up to see a swift smile appear on her husband's face.

'I expect you're right, Lydia,' he agreed softly. 'It's kind of you to pass it off so lightly – kind and understanding, my dear, and I'm sure, when she's feeling less tired, Sister will readily acknowledge this and apologize for her rudeness.'

Shani's chin lifted, but nothing would have drawn words from her while Lydia remained in the room. Ignoring them both, she began counting the swabs over again, hoping her action would this time have the desired effect.

'I'll go now, Andreas. Shall I see you before this evening?'

He glanced at the briefcase under her arm, and then at his watch.

'Were you going over to my house now?'

'Yes, I was on my way there when I remembered the message I'd promised to deliver to Sister Reeves.'

'Make some tea,' he said after a slight hesitation. 'I'll be with you in a few minutes. You have your key?'

'Yes.' A gloating look cast in Shani's direction, a dazzling smile for Andreas, and Lydia was gone.

Shani then said, her anger having subsided,

'I shouldn't have spoken to you like that, especially in front of Miss Murray.' She expected a stern, disciplinary expression to enter his eyes, but all she saw was that odd light enter their depths again.

'I had no idea you disliked Miss Murray,' he said in a toneless voice. 'You appear to dislike her most strongly.'

She felt puzzled. Where was the frigid manner to which she had now become used?

'I'm not sufficiently interested in Miss Murray either

to like or dislike her.'

'You're not? Why, then, did you order her out?'

'She had no right to be in here.'

'Her reason for being here appears to be quite valid. She obligingly delivered you a message.'

'What I should have said was that she had no right to stay – after giving me the message, I mean.'

Andreas stared down at one of the trolleys and absently scanned its contents.

'Why did she stay?'

'It doesn't matter,' returned Shani a trifle impatiently. Why was Andreas concerning himself with so trifling an occurrence? 'You wouldn't be interested.'

'You told me she insulted you,' he said, ignoring her comments. 'What did she say to make you so angry?'

'I can't tell you that.' Where was the loyalty he owed to Lydia? Or could it be that he did not owe her any loyalty? – that she meant no more to him than she did to any of the other doctors for whom she worked? That she was doing some sort of work for Andreas was now evident. He wrote articles and reports, and of course he would want those typed. Shani frowned. The relationship could not be merely a business one because Andreas and Lydia went out together on occasions, and it was known that he had several times dined with Lydia's parents at their converted Turkish house in the mountains of Lapithos.

'You can't tell me, eh? There must be a good reason why you can't, Shani?' She said nothing and after a moment Andreas asked softly, 'Perhaps, then, there is something you will tell me.' He looked straight at her and she had difficulty in meeting his gaze. 'Are you really going home because of the break with Brian?'

Her heart missed a beat. He seemed to be probing into her very soul. His question was odd, and unexpected. He was a doctor. ... Could there be a dawning suspicion in his mind? Were he to know about the child he would offer to have her with him, even though by his own admission he was no longer interested in her. If she refused his offer he would take the child from her, perhaps for six months of the year. The law could grant him this, should she raise an objection.

'Yes,' she lied in desperation. 'Certainly it's because of Brian.'

His gaze remained on her for a long, frightening moment and then his lip curled.

'I suppose you consider me responsible for this upheaval in your life?'

'You are responsible,' she whispered, and there was no need for her to lie this time.

'I'd have given you credit for more courage,' he shot at her with a half-sneer. 'You'd have got over it in time. There was no need for so rash a decision.'

Her eyes kindled strangely.

'Why should you care, Andreas? After all, you yourself said you no longer had any interest in me, so why should you be concerned about my job, or my future?' Her voice was low and husky, holding a plea, a desperate little plea which her husband missed.

'You're quite right, I have lost interest in you – so why should I concern myself about your future?' With a sweeping glance of a contempt he left her standing there, one trembling hand resting on the trolley, her tiny ray of hope dying as quickly as it had been born.

CHAPTER NINE

WORKING with Andreas had been trying before, but after the little scene in the theatre it had become positively unpleasant and Shani began to wish she had taken Matron's hinted advice and left straight away. But she was having to work out her notice now because her replacement was not coming for another four weeks. When on duty Andreas snapped at her all the time, when off duty he adopted an attitude of complete indifference towards her. This was more apparent when there happened to be a social gathering, which often occurred as one or another of the staff would always be having a little get together, sometimes in Matron's room and sometimes at the local *taverna*. On these occasions all formality was dropped and Christian names were used. Shani was as usual popular with everyone – everyone except Andreas, who deliberately avoided speaking to her.

This pleased Lydia, but always there was a puzzled light in her eyes and she would often glance from Shani to Andreas, a frown crossing her handsome flawless countenance.

'What's wrong with Lydia?' asked Jenny one evening when they were having a party in the garden of the *taverna*. It was Sister Glover's birthday and many of the staff, including Shani and Andreas, were at her party. 'She gives you the most peculiar looks.'

'We don't get along,' shrugged Shani, watching in disgust as Lydia made eyes at Andreas.

'Who does get along with her?' Chrystalla put in. 'No one.'

'Andreas Manou,' corrected Jenny. 'I wonder what she'll do when he's gone.'

'Follow him, probably,' interposed Dr. Gordon with a grin, but he shook his head for all that. 'Can't see the attraction at all. She just isn't Andreas's type.'

'She does some kind of work for him.' Shani's eyes were drawn to Lydia again. She was speaking, and as though in emphasis she laid a beautifully-manicured hand on Andreas's arm.

'She does work for several of us, but we don't reward her by taking her out.'

Andreas glanced across to where Shani's little group were talking, almost as if he sensed he was the object of interest. He looked indifferently through Shani and turned again to his companion. Her glass was empty and he took it to the bar.

'I think it's only now and then that he takes her out,' submitted Chrystalla. 'Andreas's lights are on nearly every evening. I think he works in his home.'

'Lydia has charming parents, and probably when he does dine at her house it's the parents he really goes to see.' This, surprisingly, came from Jenny, who added, in contradiction to former statements she had made, 'I entirely agree, she just isn't Andreas's type.'

'Yes,' said Dr. Gordon musingly, 'you're right about her parents; they are charming. I've dined with them myself on a couple of occasions.'

The four folk musicians started to play and several couples got up, dancing on the dusty ground, while in one corner three Cypriots began to perform one of the more lively Greek dances.

After a while the music stopped and the 'floor' was cleared. Yannis, the custodian of Kyrenia Castle, got up and instantly there was a roar of pleasure from everyone. Yannis was the star attraction at any party. Jovial, and so very European in his ways, having worked in England for many years, he was yet the typical Greek Cypriot – open, generous, and a little naïve. He was also handsome, and as agile as any twenty-year-old youth. Everyone knew and liked Yannis; he was one of tourism's greatest assets.

He danced tirelessly, leaping into the air and twisting to the quick and lively strains of the *bouzouki* band.

At last he sat down next to Andreas and they talked for a while, but as the music struck up again he came across to Shani.

'Come,' he said, laughing. 'Let's show them!'

She blushed and shook her head.

'No, Yannis, I—'

'Shani! Yes, we want Shani!' came the resounding chorus. 'She's the only one who does it like a Cypriot!'

'Please, Yannis, not in front of all these people.' But she wasted words. Yannis had her on her feet.

The dance was slow and difficult, but both Shani and Yannis were experts. They held handkerchiefs, twisting them and shaking them in a way that gave special emphasis to the graceful swerving of their bodies. The movements of the handkerchiefs were important and concise, in complete harmony with the rhythm of the steps. The garden setting by the sea, the folk musicians in their colourful costumes, the twinkling lights half hidden in the vines, the quiet rhythmical handclapping of the audience . . . all these contributed to the success of the graceful performance. The dance had its origins in antiquity, its movements often reflecting pagan rites – sacrificial, barbaric. Shani and Yannis danced it much the same as it had been danced over two thousand years ago at the altar of some deity of ancient Greece. Forgetting her audience, and even her anxieties, Shani danced for the sheer joy of being alive, her face flushed, her eyes sparkling and her lovely slender body perfect in movement. She and her partner never touched, but they danced in complete harmony, their steps light and accurate.

Suddenly she caught her husband's eye and saw there both admiration and surprise, and . . . but it couldn't possibly be pride!

Her thoughts went involuntarily to that day in Cos, when the sponge-diver from Kalymos danced so beautifully for them. And she knew instinctively that Andreas too was back in Cos. She almost made a mistake then; Andreas noticed the slip, but even before he had smiled encouragingly she made her recovery. The applause was deafening when they finished. Everyone shouted for more.

Shani sat down, flushed and happy; all were cheering still – all except Lydia whose face was dark with envy.

'That was marvellous!' exclaimed Yannis, handing her a drink. 'Shani's the best of all the English in Cyprus!'

Did Andreas dance much? she wondered. He would never dance here, though, she was just deciding when to her surprise he and Dr. Charalambedes and the indefatigable Yannis began the dance which was found only in Cyprus, and even there it was fast dying out. It was the Dance of the Sickle, and it struck Shani that the sickles must have been brought in earlier, ready for the performance.

'Has it some special meaning?' asked Jenny of Chrystalla. The sickles were being moved sometimes as if in harvesting while at other times the movement took the form of a whip encircling the body.

'It's a kind of symbolic dance,' explained Chrystalla at length. 'But its origins are lost. The dance has to do with fertility and was performed at festivities held in honour of the earth goddess.'

'Why is it danced only in Cyprus?'

'I don't know. It originated in Sparta and the Dorians brought it here. In Sparta Artemis was the Goddess of Fertility, and her equivalent here is Aphrodite, so perhaps that's why it's lasted longer in Cyprus. You would expect the dance to become strongly rooted here because Aphrodite was born here.'

'But Aphrodite's the Goddess of Love!'

'And of Fertility – and of Beauty.' Chrystalla laughed. 'She has many forms.'

This dance was also difficult, but it was clearly a man's dance, and when the sickle was used in the whip movement it represented the scourging at the ancient altar of Artemis where the youths of Sparta entered contests of endurance and hardship.

'It's so pagan!' exclaimed Brenda in a whisper. 'Our Mr. Manou even looks like a pagan!'

'How do you know what a pagan looks like?' laughed Dr. Gordon. 'Yannis's face is just as hard and set as that of Andreas.'

He even looks like a pagan . . . Shani saw him again

crossing the lawn, and she remembered how the sky seemed to darken. But she was only eighteen, and a very young eighteen at that. He had frightened her, sheltered as she was by her father, living very close to him since the death of her mother, never leaving him alone unless it was absolutely necessary. No wonder Andreas had frightened her. But she was not frightened now. His grim exterior was forbidding, but she had known the gentleness beneath, had been given a small sample of the care and concern that could have been hers had she only discovered her own feelings a little sooner . . . before her husband had lost interest in her.

She watched the dancers, fascinated, her eyes often moving to her husband's face, its expression reminding her that the credo of the ancient Hellenes was freedom, pride and noble competition. Dancing, it was said, was a medium through which could be balanced spirit and matter; it expressed the human feelings and emotions, drawing out beauty from the very depths of the soul. It revealed the urge of the subconscious— Abruptly she tried to shake off the idea that her husband's face was sad behind the mask of set concentration . . . sad and desolate. Frowning, Shani tore her eyes away, and looked down at her hands.

But the change of vision merely brought into focus the picture of Andreas as she had seen him one evening after she had been to his house to discuss the question of an annulment. She had looked back, and he had been sitting there, with his head sunk in his hands.

The dance ended and once again there were cheers and hand-clapping, and shouts for more. Shani looked up to meet her husband's gaze. He was not looking in the least desolate or sad, but smiling faintly at something Yannis was saying, and Shani managed to dismiss the impression that Andreas was unhappy.

Refreshments were served and then a more sedate and much simpler dance was performed with about a dozen people forming the long row. Andreas asked Lydia to join in, but obviously she had never been interested enough to learn even the simple dances and Shani found herself standing next to her husband, his hand on her shoulder and her hand resting lightly on his. And as they danced he bent his head to hers and whispered, in a tone faintly mocking yet unmistakably tinged with praise,

'You're full of surprises, Shani ... and some are really very pleasant ones.' His comment, so unexpected after the indifference he normally adopted, brought no response from Shani and he did not speak again during the dance.

'... some are really very pleasant ones.' She mused on this. Among the unpleasant surprises was the discovery that she approved Brian's action in threatening Andreas. It hurt that he should believe this, that he was still under the impression she would countenance such an unscrupulous method of obtaining her freedom. Her mouth curved bitterly. It was ironical that Brian's interference had come after she had decided not to marry him, and when she was already considering the possibility of living with her husband. Would things have been different had not Brian chosen to interfere? It seemed so very strange that after forcing her into marriage, and then taking the trouble to search for her, Andreas should lose interest – and that quite suddenly. The change had been sudden, no doubt about that. On the holiday he had been extremely interested in her. Could it be that he had said he had lost interest simply because he was hurt at the idea that she still preferred Brian, after the wonderful holiday they had spent together? – the holiday which, she now knew, had raised her husband's hopes of a change in her feelings towards him. At her refusal of his suggestion he had seemed defeated . . . but could the last of his hopes have died only after Brian's telephone call? Perhaps, she thought eagerly, she should try again. . . . But no, it was too great a risk. Andreas had been so emphatic in his declaration that he no longer wanted her and were she to confess all she would once again be in his power. For the sake of the child he would offer her a home; either she must accept, living with a man who did not want her, or she must share their child with him. That he would be unrelenting about the question of the child she did not for one moment doubt. Greek men were wonderful fathers; they loved their children, so it was beyond the bounds of possibility that he would cut himself off from the only child he was ever likely to have, being through his own act bound irrevocably to Shani. No, she dared not take so great a risk.

When the dance came to an end Andreas remained for a while talking to Dr. Gordon, and then automatically walked with him over to where Shani and her little group were sitting. Jenny gave her friend a nudge. Lydia had risen and was coming over to join them.

'She's a trier,' said Jenny spitefully. 'I'll grant her that.'

'You're being bitchy,' laughed Chrystalla. The word had recently been explained to her and she welcomed the opportunity of using it.

'Who's being bitchy? – and about whom?' Dr. Gordon sat down facing Shani, but for a moment Andreas remained standing, watching his wife as she in turn watched the languid approach of Lydia Murray. Shani glanced up, and for some inexplicable reason she blushed. 'Not you, Shani—' Dr. Gordon broke off abruptly, casting Andreas a swift glance and then looking at Lydia. Through Shani's mind flashed Matron's evasive words to the doctor on the day she had fainted in Matron's room. With an effort Shani laughed, shaking her head, and to her intense relief Dr. Gordon's face cleared.

But what of Andreas? His expression was most odd indeed, portraying the same enigmatic quality that had settled on his face during the scene in the theatre with Lydia. It was almost as if he suspected his wife of jealousy! Could he possibly be thinking that now she had lost Brian she was beginning to resent his association with Lydia? No doubt that would afford him extreme satisfaction, and was probably the reason why he had suddenly become especially nice to Lydia that day, and very condescending to his wife – even suggesting she apologize to the detestable woman! Shani bristled. Jealous? He need harbour no such gratifying ideas. If he wasn't interested in her, neither was she interested in him – nor in his woman friends!

Andreas brought up a chair for Lydia and then sat down beside her. But his eyes were on Shani, thoughtfully examining her flushed countenance.

'Andreas,' said Sister Louzides curiously, 'you're a Greek, so how come you to do the sickle dance so expertly? It isn't even danced in your country, so you couldn't have learnt it there.'

'I lived in Cyprus for several years, as a boy.'

'Ah, that explains it.' She took a glass from the tray offered her by one of the café proprietor's young sons. 'You'll not be able to unbend like this when you get back to London. The English are so inhibited— With apologies to all my English friends here,' she added sweetly, and they scowled at her, but only in fun.

'No, indeed. I shall have to be very much on my dignity.'

He would always be dignified, thought Shani. During the dance his inborn dignity was revealed in every movement, in the harmony and measure, in the strong yet graceful sweep of the sickle.

'And Shani's also leaving us,' sighed Jenny, her regret plainly including Andreas, despite her repeated grumbles about his severity and arrogance of manner. 'Wouldn't it be a coincidence if you met again in London? – if you found yourselves working together in the same hospital?'

Glancing instinctively at Andreas, Shani realized he was deliberately avoiding her eyes, and she recalled his strongly-expressed hope that on leaving Loutras he would never set eyes on her again. He had not known then that she would be leaving first, and that his hopes would materialize even sooner than he had anticipated.

'It's possible,' agreed Brenda, 'because you'll be working in London, won't you, Shani?'

'I—' About to say there was no likelihood of her working in London, Shani stopped, aware of Lydia's dark eyes fixed upon her with an almost malevolent expression. 'I might be working in London – some time,' she said in cool and even tones, quite forgetful of Dr. Gordon, who tactfully refrained either from looking at Shani or joining in the conversation.

Andreas glanced up quickly and a hint of colour crept into Shani's lovely cheeks. Worried, was he? – in case she should intrude into his life again? Little did he know that several years must elapse before she could consider returning to work. But Shani was glad she had given Lydia something to think about. 'Acting in that proprietorial manner – and with *my* husband!' she quivered on seeing Lydia handing her empty glass to Andreas. Lydia was smiling at him, but she kept swallowing thickly, and it was not difficult to see that she was deeply affected by Shani's rather spiteful little declaration that she might possibly be working in London.

A ready smile took away Shani's frown as Yannis joined her little group. He talked and drank and smoked his pipe, then after a while, to Shani's great consternation, he suggested she and Andreas should dance together.

She could not dance with Andreas – in any case, he would not want to dance with her. . . . Lydia was scowling at Yannis for making the suggestion, but of course he did not notice. To Shani's surprise Andreas was ready to dance with her, a clear invitation conveyed in the look he gave her. It would be altogether too trying to dance with her husband and Shani began to shake her head. Lydia was still scowling; Andreas's hand was extended and Shani took it, allowing him to lead her on to the floor. Yannis threw Shani his large handkerchief and she deftly caught it as it fluttered down, almost on to Lydia's knee. Shani smiled at her enemy in the most satisfied way and Lydia's mouth compressed. 'I'm being bitchy tonight,' declared Shani to herself. 'And I'm thoroughly enjoying it!'

The dance was a variation of the Labyrinth Dance of Knossos, performed by Theseus and the youths and maidens he had rescued from the monstrous bull-headed Minotaur of Crete, the occasion of that dance, at the altar of Apollo, being the first time in Greek history that men and women had danced together.

For the most part the body movements consisted of labyrinthine evolutions, and the suppleness of both dancers was outstandingly emphasized in the leaping twists and turns as they followed with unerring precision an imaginary maze-pattern on the ground. It was a complicated dance, originally arranged for many people so that Andreas and Shani were compelled to introduce certain variations of their own – caprices and tricks faultlessly executed though differing in form. At times the woman must be meek, her eyes downcast, her movements hesitantly modest, while in sharp contrast the spinnings and leapings of the man were vigorous and strong, as would be expected of the brave slayer of the Minotaur.

Shani's handkerchief was employed in a unique and remarkably effective way, depicting the grief of Ariadne on being abandoned by her lover after she had led him safely out of the Labyrinth by means of a ball of thread. The handkerchief represented a veil, torn in her distress and used by Ariadne to wipe away her tears. In the final sad beat of the dance it was waved in a series of despairing gestures as his ship took Theseus further and further away from the island on which he and Ariadne had spent the night. The end seemed so linked with her own experience that Shani's eyes became bright with unshed tears, and yet it was an animated little face that looked up into her husband's eyes as, with the fading of the melancholy strains of the *bouzouki* music the deafening applause broke out. Her cheeks were flushed, her lips quivering slightly, and parted, for she was a little breathless after her exertions. For a long moment he stared down at her, oblivious of the applause and then, shaking his head in a gesture of mingled impatience and mystification, he led her back to their party.

'Shani, you were marvellous!'

'You danced beautifully together!'

'Anyone would think you'd practised beforehand,' said Jenny as Shani sat down beside her, and then, in a whisper, 'Lydia's seething. You know something? She's jealous of you.'

'Then she can't be very sure of Andreas,' returned Shani, throwing Lydia a superior look and deciding it was extraordinarily pleasant to be a cat for a change. She was unaware that her husband had noticed her action, and that it had brought a very thoughtful frown to his face.

'I'm fast changing my opinion of Andreas Manou,' whispered Jenny. 'He's not bad at all – when he's off duty,' she added as if finding it necessary to modify her statement. 'I'll bet you never thought he could unbend to this extent.'

A reflective smile touched Shani's lips. If only Jenny could have seen him riding round Cos on a bicycle, or sunning his brown body clad in the briefest of trunks. If she could have seen him digging away with his hands to uncover a mosaic ... seen him eating in a wayside *taverna* ... heard him talking to the sponge-diver of Kalymnos.

'I think most doctors give the wrong impression,' she said at length. 'At work they're nearly always aloof and – well, rather stiff.'

'You sound as if you're making excuses for Andreas.' Jenny eyed her curiously. Shani was still flushed, still a little breathless.

'I was speaking generally.' She stopped, listening to the music. The record player was being used while the folk musicians took a rest. Petros had put on an English dance tune and one or two couples were getting up.

'Now, Yannis, this is where we score.' Dr. Gordon stood up and held out a hand to Jenny. 'You can now see how *we* do it!'

'What does he mean – this is where we score?' asked Yannis of Shani. 'Does he think I can't do your dances, after living in England for five years?'

'Did you live there as long as that?'

'Five years – and it rained all the time.'

'No, it didn't.'

'You're right. It was snowing part of the time – when it wasn't foggy or frosty or blowing a gale.' His brown face was wrinkled with suppressed laughter. 'You think that's not true?'

'I know it's not.' She looked up and her heartbeats quickened. Andreas was going to ask her to dance. . . . He gave her an indifferent stare and smilingly· extended a hand to Lydia. 'Where in England did you live?' she asked, turning to Yannis as if she had not noticed that Andreas had gone to Lydia.

'Manchester.'

'Oh, well, you chose the very worst place. It does rain

there, I admit.'

'I suppose you have compensations,' remarked Yannis with a surprising hint of nostalgia. 'You have the greenness. That was something I missed on first returning to Cyprus. But of the two – the greenness and the sun,' he added, 'I prefer to have the sun.' He watched the dancers for a while and then, 'Come, Shani, I can't have Dr. Gordon hinting that I can't do your dances.'

They came close to Lydia and her partner. Over Lydia's head Andreas's eyes met those of his wife and again she noticed that odd expression. He bent his head and whispered something to his partner. Her laugh rang out and several glances were sent in her direction. Stupid woman, thought Shani. Couldn't she see that her efforts were providing everyone with considerable amusement!

But after this little episode the evening fell flat for Shani. She had scoffed at the idea, now formed, she felt sure, in her husband's mind, that she could be jealous of Lydia, but there was no doubt that the sight of the girl in Andreas's arms filled Shani with an emotion that in all honesty she had to admit was jealousy. He could never marry the girl, and it was obvious that he did not love her, but he paid her more attention than did any of the other doctors for whom she worked, especially lately, reflected Shani with a frown. Could it be that after becoming resigned to the idea that Shani could never be his he had decided to satisfy his innate desires by indulging in an affair with another woman? A light affair of this kind was usual with Greek men, and they invariably chose foreign women because they would never tarnish the chastity of their own women. Recollections of that night at the villa intruded and the thought of Lydia in Andreas's embrace was unbearable. She cast it off. 'He wouldn't, not after taking that oath' . . . but the next moment her common sense reminded her he was only human. And he was a Greek, with the inherited passions of those of the East. . . .

Two sailors walked into the garden and bought a drink at the bar.

'A party?' said one, his lean body moving rhythmically to the music.

'*Kopiaste!*' Yannis stopped dancing and steered his partner over to the bar.

'Thanks, we'd love to join you, but we've a date at Clito's. A party of tourists from the Dome are going there and we've promised Clito we'll put on the local colour for them.' The sailor glanced round. 'Why don't *you* all join *us*?'

Everyone agreed and a few moments later they had all piled into the cars, taking the two sailors with them.

Clito's Bar was far removed from the plush hotels of Cyprus, but no holiday on the island was complete without a visit to this cellar bar which, to every newcomer, had all the appearances of a 'dive'. The walls were whitewashed and hung with dusty netting and even dustier lights. The 'tables' were wine barrels whose only embellishments were stains and cigarette burns. The floor was uncovered stone. From a brilliantly-lighted box in one corner *bouzouki* music blared forth and in the centre of the floor half a dozen sailors were already giving the tourists what they had come to see. They danced superbly, their body movements often orgiastic. The tourists sat around, drinking and smoking and thoroughly delighted with the atmosphere.

'This is the real Cyprus!' exclaimed one old man enthusiastically, his knees white as yet beneath his baggy shorts. 'We must come here every night.'

'Which is Clito?' asked a woman sitting next to Shani. She was looking enviously at her brown arms and feeling she could provide the information required. 'We're told he's blind.'

'He is blind, yes. Here he is, coming down the stairs.'

A sailor immediately left the dancers and went to Clito's aid. The old man looked happy, as he always did when his bar was full.

'How does he come to be blind? We were told he was beaten up in his own bar.'

'Yes, there was a brawl.'

'But who did it?'

Shani had already hesitated about answering that even before she caught Yannis's warning glance. He spoke for her.

'We don't mention it,' he said, quite affably. 'Would you like to meet Clito?'

'Yes, indeed.'

Yannis got up and brought Clito over to where they were sitting. The tourists were delighted, most of them having read Lawrence Durrell's famous book in which Clito was often mentioned. The old man welcomed them and they all had drinks on him.

'The atmosphere of your bar is marvellous,' the woman told him. 'We wanted local colour and we've certainly got it here.' In the dark corners unshaven sailors in dark jerseys slouched, cigarettes dangling. In

172

other dim places couples flirted and kissed. It was all a 'show', put on by the loyal friends of Clito in order to bring him in the money for an operation on his eyes. But there was no doubt that an evening at Clito's was pleasant and entertaining. The sailors readily taught the visitors to dance, taking the steps slowly and showing amazing patience. The wine was good, and cheap – Clito's 'special' from the barrel. There was laughter and music, dancing and drinking, with the locals mingling with the guests.

'I don't think anyone could leave here without vowing to return,' said Shani to Clito. 'It's great fun.'

'You'll tell your friends?'

'I always do.' Close beside her a relative of Clito's, an old man, dark and toothless, was making his usual contribution to the entertainment, his movements, as he balanced a glass of wine on his head, bringing roars of laughter from the men but leaving the women completely baffled.

'Sexy, must be,' said Jenny. 'But isn't it maddening when you can't understand what it's all about?'

Vulgar, said Lydia's expression, and Jenny added, softly, 'Obviously she's not so dense – but look at her face. This sort of entertainment's clearly not her cup of tea.' And it wasn't, for she yawned repeatedly and in the end she turned to Andreas, saying,

'Shall we go? It's past one o'clock.'

'You don't want to go yet,' put in Dr. Charalambedes. 'The fun's only just begun. It goes on till two or three in the morning.'

'I couldn't stay that long. Andreas, will you take me home?'

173

He hesitated, caught the sudden sparkle in his wife's eye and said softly,

'Very well, Lydia, we'll go if you wish. Does anyone else want a lift?' he added, glancing round.

'Not me.' Yannis shook his head. 'I'm enjoying myself.'

'Nor me.' Jenny also shook her head.

No one else wanted a lift and Lydia's face was a study of satisfaction at the idea of a moonlight drive with Andreas.

'I'd like a lift,' said Shani, rising. 'I've just realized I'm rather tired.'

Yes, she thought as she followed them to the car. I am being bitchy tonight!

CHAPTER TEN

WITH only ten days to go before her departure for England Shani was fully organized, her boxes having already been collected and taken to the port at Famagusta where they would be dispatched on the next ship for Liverpool. Her aunt was only too willing to have her, but her letter had contained a good many acid comments about men in general and Andreas in particular. With all his money, she had emphasized, he should be made to pay. Shani's letter to her aunt had been the most difficult she had ever written; it was so hard to explain the situation without putting Andreas in a bad light, and judging by the reply she hadn't been as successful as she thought. There would be some uncomfortable moments on her arrival, Shani knew, but so great was her aunt's dislike of men that she would be sure to say in the end that Shani was far better off on her own.

It was customary for a member of staff who was leaving to give a party, and Shani asked Matron's permission to do this. Matron looked somewhat surprised, thinking, no doubt, that the situation could scarcely be comfortable either for Shani or Andreas. She and Shani were sitting on the verandah, but although it was warm the sky was darkened by clouds and the farmers hopefully declared it would rain before the morning. Already the deluge had hit Troodos and it was so cold up there that snow was expected earlier than usual.

'You'll return to nursing?' Matron asked conversationally after she had given her permission for the farewell party.

'Later, yes.'

'Your aunt will look after the child?'

'I haven't asked her, but if she won't I'll have to wait until it's at school.'

'And then do part-time work, of course.'

Shani nodded, her attention caught by Lydia's car pulling up on the park at the side of the hospital. The girl got out and walked briskly in the direction of Andreas's house. Matron cast Shani a sideways glance, causing her colour to rise. It was not difficult to read Matron's thoughts. She was thinking some hard things about Andreas – and that Shani had been foolish in the extreme.

'You must write to me, and let me know how you're getting along.'

Shani made no answer; once she left the island she would make a new life for herself, using her husband's name. There would have to be a complete break; she could not even write to Jenny, her best friend. Tears filmed her eyes. Would Andreas feel sorry, she wondered, were he to discover how his act had disorganized her life? All he knew was that she was returning to England; he would naturally assume she would be working there. Perhaps, she thought, indulging in a tiny bout of self-pity, he would have serious trouble with his conscience if he ever learned the truth. But it was to be hoped he never would learn the truth, for the child's sake.

As she made her way back to the annexe where she had been visiting some of the patients in her off-duty time, Shani glanced automatically at the car park. It was now accepted that the relationship between

Andreas and Lydia was strengthening rapidly. They were together far too much for Andreas's interest to be one of mere business. Ever since the night of Sister Glover's party, mused Shani as she entered the annexe. She herself had experienced a brief moment of triumph when she and her husband had danced together ... but Lydia's was the final victory. 'But he can't marry her,' said Shani, borrowing a little of her friend's spite. 'She's in for a shock if that's what she has in mind.'

Luciana's aunt was in the annexe, having fallen down some steps and cut her head and arms. But her injuries were not serious and she was thoroughly enjoying the rest and good food, and the luxury of being waited upon for the first time in her life. She was old and wrinkled, but from her dark face a pair of the most expressive eyes Shani had ever seen shone happily as Shani approached the bed.

'Sister Reeves. ...' The old woman's hand clasped that of her visitor. 'I thought you had gone without having a little talk with me.'

'I wouldn't do that; I wanted to have a few words with Matron while she wasn't busy.'

'My auntie was saying, before you came, that she would like to kiss you.' Luciana, who had arrived in Shani's absence, was sitting on the opposite side of the bed.

'Why?' asked Shani curiously, aware of the soft caress of the woman's fingers on the back of her hand.

'She loves all the English – my auntie. You see, your Queen sends her money every month, and she never once fails, or is late. And from our own Government she gets not one single *mil*! So it's because she loves the

English that she wants to kiss you.'

Shani bent her head and the old woman kissed her cheek, her face smiling yet serene. There was a great depth to some of these old ladies, and Shani had often wondered what sort of an impact they would have made on their island had they been emancipated, and educated.

'Your father was killed in the war?' Shani straightened up, but retained her hold on the woman's hand.

'He was in the British Navy, and my auntie was left with six children. Just think of that, Sister Reeves, all alone with six children.'

And I, thought Shani, am feeling sorry for myself at the idea of having to bring up one on my own.

'They were all small?'

'The eldest was eight. But your Queen's father sent them money for food and clothes, and for their education. All my cousins received an excellent education and now have the best paid posts. That's why we all love the English people.'

Shani smiled.

'Yes, I've noticed, Luciana, that you and your family are among the few people I know who don't keep reminding me of "the roads the British made for us". You know,' she added, her smile deepening, 'those narrow strips of tarmac which unfortunately have got your drivers into the habit of keeping to the middle of the road. On first coming here my friend and I hired a car so that we could see something of your island. I complained of this habit, in a nice sort of way, of course, but soon learned to hold my tongue, being told it was all *my* fault because, they would say, "*You* made the roads for us".'

Luciana looked pained, even though Shani herself was amused.

'That was not very kind.'

'It was all quite good-humoured, Luciana. Your little argument with the Guardian of the Fields was the nearest thing to a quarrel I've ever heard since coming here.'

At that Luciana chuckled.

'That's because we're all related, even though distantly, and family ties are very strong in Cyprus.' With the soft sound of a bell ringing Luciana rose from her chair. 'I have to go now, Auntie; tomorrow my mother will come.'

'Don't forget to water my garden, Luciana.'

'I'll water it, but it's going to rain tomorrow.'

'Perhaps, but water it all the same.' She looked up. 'Are you going also, Sister?'

'It's time you had a little sleep,' Shani returned gently, taking her hand from that of the old woman. 'You've done enough talking for the present.'

Shani punched up the pillow and made her comfortable. For a long moment she stood looking down into the old woman's face, serene and composed as already she became lost in a half-sleep. Shani felt that one of her greatest regrets at leaving the island was the idea of saying goodbye for ever to these wonderful old people. They represented the simple village life and customs, and there was no up and coming generation to take their place. Cyprus was caught in the whirlwind of progress. It was a happy circumstance in many ways ... but so very sad in others.

Three days to go. Shani had had her party the previous evening in the sisters' sitting-room, with Lydia naturally not invited. Andreas had been cool, but on occasions attentive, extending to her the courtesy and polite care he normally kept for Lydia. His eyes would meet hers, that odd light in their depths, as he handed her some refreshment, or sat talking on the balcony where several little groups were sitting under a starlit sky.

'The rain doesn't appear to have done very much good.' Shani felt awkward as, Jenny and Sister Louzides having drifted away, she found herself alone with Andreas. 'I expect it's because the ground's so baked. The rain can't penetrate.'

'That's why we have the torrents sweeping down the roads. Part of the Vasilios by-pass has been washed away, one side of the road having completely collapsed.'

Such stiff conversation, Shani thought. The atmosphere seemed suddenly to become electrified.

'And of course when the rain stops the sun comes out immediately and begins baking the ground again. It will be bad for the island if the winter's as dry as last year.' Shani fingered the stem of her glass in an abstracted sort of way. She had the impression that her husband had something of tremendous importance to say to her, but could not find the opportunity, with all these people about. 'There's been a good deal of snow on Troodos, though, and if this keeps on the meltwater will eventually do a lot of good.'

Dr. Gordon joined them, and then one or two others came from the sitting-room. Andreas gave a little sigh and after a while excused himself, saying he had work to do.

At five o'clock the following morning he was called out urgently to Nicosia and on arrival there he rang through to Loutras saying he would not be back until late the following evening. Shani was off duty, but on seeing her as she came off the ward, where she had been talking to one of the English patients, Matron asked Shani to take some reports to Mr. Manou's room.

'Just put them on his desk. He'll attend to them when he gets back.'

Shani laid them down ... and then her eye caught the key, lying there on the inkstand. The key of the villa up on Troodos.

Her bracelet. ... Suddenly it seemed imperative that she should have it in her possession – her husband's only present to her, apart from her wedding and engagement rings, of course.

She stood by the desk, then hesitantly picked up the key, holding it in her hand and staring fascinatedly down at it. She could go up to the villa and be back before Andreas returned. There was a bus in half an hour's time ...

The roads were clear, but snow lay thick on the mountains, and great black cumulus clouds came threateningly lower and lower as, leaving the bus, Shani made for the narrow track along which Andreas had driven on that unforgettable evening. The villa appeared through the gloom, a bleak little dwelling, isolated and forlorn. The interior was dark and cold and a shiver passed through Shani as she hurried into the bedroom. With the bracelet in her pocket she came out of the villa again, locking the door and leaving without one backward glance. Snow came down in great flakes on to the silent mountains and into the valley. The bus would go up to Prodhromos and then return. She must catch it, for she knew it would be the last one that day, with visibility now down to a mere few yards. It had not been a good idea, coming up to Troodos, she chided herself, and yet she was glad she had her bracelet. The downward journey would be tedious and slow, but once safely back at the hospital she would have no regrets about her impulsive decision to go up to the villa.

She started to run, but with only a short distance between her and the villa she caught her foot on a hidden boulder and, in an effort to regain her balance, she went too near the edge and within seconds she was hurtling down the side of the mountain. Her scream, deadened by the snow, faded altogether as blackness closed in around her.

Familiar hospital smells assailed her nostrils as she regained consciousness. Familiar voices too . . . vaguely familiar . . . Matron . . . doctor . . . Monikomo. From a long way off her husband's voice reached her.

'Shani. . . .' He stopped. 'Matron, would you mind leaving?'

The white-clad figure disappearing through the door . . . the pain . . . the sensation of loss. Her eyes, unmoving, stared at those above her. Dazed as she was, their tiredness escaped her, as did the grim set of her husband's mouth. She did not notice the little white lines close to his jaw or the uncontrollable movement in his throat. She said, her voice husky with pain,

'Did you operate, Andreas?'

'Yes, Shani, I had to. There was no one else up here—'

'So now you should be satisfied. You've taken all I had.' Her accents, bitter and accusing, made him wince, but again she did not see. 'I hope that you consider you've exacted full payment for any wrong I might have done you.' For the first time in her life she spoke unfairly, but she was still very ill, too ill, even, to give a thought to how Andreas came to be here, or how she herself had been brought to Monikomo. In fact, so great was her pain that Andreas had to give her another injection and within minutes she was again insensible to everything around her.

The next time she opened her eyes she was in the hospital at Loutras. The door of her private ward was open; voices reached her from just outside.

'Sister Reeves is here, they tell me.' Lydia's voice. She must have just arrived, so it was about noon, thought Shani.

'Yes; the roads were cleared, so she came down by ambulance this morning.'

'Have I heard aright, Andreas? I'm sure I heard two of the nurses talking about a child?'

'She's lost the child, unfortunately.'

'Unfortunately! I should think she's very glad. How disgusting! – but I always thought she was like that—'

'Shani,' came the softly-spoken interruption, 'is my wife. The child was mine.'

'Your—!' Silence. Andreas glanced into the room. 'Your *wife*!'

'Yes, Lydia, my wife. And now, if you'll excuse me, I must go to her. She's coming round:'

Andreas closed the door and came slowly towards the bed. Shani felt his cool hand on her brow before, drawing up a chair, he sat down, his face tired, but not grey and haggard as on the last time she had seen it.

'How do you feel now?' The doctor ... the bedside manner.

'Much better. The pain's gone.' An awkward little pause and then, 'Thank you, Andreas. You saved my life, I think.' She made a movement, half turning into the pillow. 'I didn't mean those awful things I said up there. Forgive me.'

'There's nothing to forgive, my darling. You were very ill indeed for some hours after the operation—' A shudder passed through him, but he was smiling when he added, 'You're going to make good progress now, though; we'll have you up in no time.' His voice was low, and infinitely tender. He took her hand, hesitating as if half afraid to ask the question that hovered on his lips. But presently he did ask it, and strangely enough his tones were edged with confidence.

'You love me, Shani?'

'Yes, Andreas, I love you.' Her eyes sought his. 'You guessed?'

'I thought I guessed some time ago – during that little outburst of yours in the theatre. I could have sworn you were jealous of Lydia, but you shattered my illusions when you answered my question about Brian. Why did you lie, Shani?'

'I was afraid – terribly afraid that you might suspect I was having a baby. I didn't want you to take it from me – share it, I mean. It wouldn't be good for the child to grow up with divided loyalties.' Her glance fell to his watch. A quarter to one. What day was it? She was just about to ask how she came to be found, but Andreas was already speaking.

'And so you allowed me to believe you still loved Brian.' He shook his head, half in censure, half in sadness. 'Why, my darling, didn't you have the courage to tell me?'

My darling. . . . For the second time. And that look of tenderness in his eyes. . . . Shani's heart swelled with a new joy in spite of her loss. She explained to him, and his face shadowed with remorse.

'It was pride – stupid pride that made me say I'd lost interest. I was so bitterly disillusioned, believing you agreed with Brian's threats, believing you still preferred him, after our wonderful holiday on Cos. But if only you'd told me about the baby. Why didn't you?' he asked again.

'I thought you'd offer me the alternative of living with you, just for the sake of the child—' She looked at him, her eyes moist. 'I couldn't have done that, not loving you the way I did. And I thought that if I refused to live with you you'd insist on taking the child – for part of the time.' A tear escaped on to her cheek. 'You were so emphatic about having lost interest, and – and s-saying you n-never wanted to see me again. I really believed you meant it – believed I'd discovered my own feelings too late.'

'Don't cry, my little love. Are you tired? Do you want to rest?' She shook her head and he bent to kiss her. Then he dried her tears. 'It was very wrong of me to say that,' he admitted regretfully. 'But I believed at that time that I'd come to the end of my endurance. I felt I never wanted to see you again, because only in that way could I begin to forget. But I knew I'd never be able to forget you and so even though I'd uttered those cruel words I kept on trying, endeavouring to make you jealous. Sure I'd at last succeeded, I made an effort to talk to you, on the occasion of your farewell party, but I had no opportunity—'

'I thought you wanted to tell me something,' she interrupted. 'Oh, Andreas, why didn't you?' Had he spoken then their child would not have been lost. But naturally Shani kept this sad thought to herself.

'There were too many people about. We'd talk the following day, I thought, but was called away to Nicosia. On returning earlier than I expected, I sent for you. Matron said you were out and no one knew where you'd gone. Matron thought you must have left early because the last time she saw you was when she asked you to put some reports on my desk. I wasn't worried until I suddenly missed the key.' His hand caressed hers and he paused a moment in thought. 'There was only one reason why you should go up to the villa, and that was to get your bracelet. My feelings were very mixed then, Shani. I felt this must mean you cared, but on the other hand I was terribly worried at the thought of your going up to Troodos alone, with the weather as it was. Then I learned that the buses had stopped running and decided to drive up to the villa—'

'In that snowstorm? Oh, Andreas. . . .'

'I thought to find nothing worse than your being stranded there, without food, but—' He broke off, unable to continue for a while. 'Little did I know what I was to find. You weren't at the villa, and I was afraid – afraid for the first time in my life. By some miracle I saw you in the headlights, there by the tree that had saved your life – it had halted your fall—' Again he broke off, little beads of perspiration standing out on his forehead as he became lost in memory. 'You could have been buried by snow, but again the tree saved you, providing shelter. I got you to Monikomo . . . and there received another shock.' He looked sadly at her. 'I had to operate, Shani dear. You do understand?'

Filled with remorse at the memory of those words she uttered on first regaining consciousness, Shani felt the tears prick her eyes again. What must he have gone through – her own husband, operating only because there was no one else available – fighting for her life as he had so often fought to save the lives of others?

'You'll never forget what I said,' she cried in anguish. 'You can't – not as long as you live!'

Tenderly he kissed away her fears.

'I've forgotten already. You were very ill, and didn't know what you were saying.'

How gentle he was! Not at all like the monster he appeared to be on the night she had fled from him, nor the man who more recently had frightened her by his savage, possessive demonstration.

'I've been foolish, from the very beginning, Andreas,' she whispered. 'I now wish with all my heart I'd stayed.'

'It was my fault. I began all wrongly. But I meant to be so gentle with you,' he added quickly. 'So loving that you would automatically learn of my feelings for you. And having learned of them, I knew you'd be kind and stay with me – even though you didn't love me.'

'That was what you meant when you said that if I stayed with you one night I'd stay for ever. I understand it now . . . but then. . . .'

'You were so young, my love – and I didn't make allowances. I should have done, as I once told you. I should have understood, being a doctor.'

They sat in silence for a while and then Shani said,

'Andreas . . . I didn't agree with what Brian did – in fact, I'd no idea of his intentions. I'd already decided to break with him before he – he threatened you. I knew, after the holiday, that I could never marry Brian, even though at that time I was so confused about my feelings for you. But I soon knew, Andreas, truly, and after that I was so excited about the baby—'

'You didn't resent what I did?' he interrupted, eyeing her curiously.

She shook her head.

'No, because I think I must already have known that it was you I wanted – not consciously, but it was there, all the same.'

'And you came to tell me – that day I said I never wanted to see you again?' She nodded, anxious to pass that off, but he added, his eyes dark with contrition, 'To think that I would hurt you – when all I wanted was to love you, and care for you.' He paused a moment, reflectively, and then uttered a deep sigh. 'As I said, darling, I kept on trying. At Sister Glover's party that evening, I felt convinced you were jealous of Lydia, and so I'm afraid I paid her rather more attention than usual—'

'You paid her attention before then,' Shani couldn't help reminding him. 'I *was* jealous, just as you thought, but long before Sister Glover's party – although I didn't know it myself. She was always at your

188

house, and you were so nice to her that day in the theatre,' she went on plaintively, unaware of the hint of amusement that touched her husband's lips. 'You told me off shockingly, and then even suggested I apologize to her!'

'That was to make you jealous, and it failed utterly – my being nice to her, I mean. And I'm sorry I told you off, sweetheart. You may have your revenge later.' She laughed then, but went on to say that it did seem as if he cared for Lydia. 'No, darling, it was nothing like that. She was doing work for me – on my typewriter, so she came to my home. I dined at her house because I found her parents charming. On the day of the wedding she asked me to take her and I agreed because it would have been churlish to refuse, my having no one else in the car.' He smiled tenderly at her. 'No, Shani, it was always you, from the moment you ran into my arms and looked up at me with those beautiful eyes. I loved you on sight – and would have told your father there and then, but I felt he would laugh because Greek men have a reputation for – well, desiring rather than loving.'

That hesitation. She would have care and – consideration. But Shani now knew he had been going to say 'care and love'.

'My father fell in love with Mother on sight,' she told him, her fingers curling tenderly round his. 'He used to say it would be the same with me. Andreas,' she added regretfully, repeating what she had already said, 'I've been very foolish, right from the start.'

'No. I was selfish, I know that now. It was brought home to me the night you ran from me. I realized then that I must let you grow up – have some girlhood before settling down to marriage. I would set about finding you later, when you were more mature.' He stopped, and suddenly he looked very young, and not at all like the austere doctor whom everyone held in awe. 'I came here with the intention of courting you, just as English girls like to be courted. That's why I took the post for a year, being based here, but of course on call to other hospitals. But you immediately asked for your freedom so that you could marry someone else. I was shattered, for the idea of your finding someone else had never occurred to me – which was pompous, I suppose—'

'No, Andreas. You naturally concluded I would remain on my own because you yourself never thought of having anyone else.' She drew her hand from his and turned away. 'You make me feel awful!'

Andreas took possession of her hand again; he also brought her face round, forcing her to look at him.

'You're not to blame for anything, Shani.' She would have spoken, but his lips were on hers, tender and warm.

'I suppose I should have told you, when we were so happy on Cos, that I loved you,' he murmured at last. 'That would have saved us both a lot of heartache.'

'But you didn't because of Brian. You thought I still cared for him.' Shani still considered she was the one to blame. She should have known, when her husband bestowed on her such care and tenderness, that it must be love he felt for her, and not merely desire, as she had from the first concluded. That holiday had been an opportunity for her to discover the real Andreas – and she had not taken advantage of it. Presently she said, on a reflective note, 'At one time I had the impression you were plotting something—'

'Plotting something?'

'I felt you'd find a way of preventing the annulment - even if my lawyer was right, and it could have been obtained by me.' Another hesitation. 'Had you—? What I mean is . . .' She could not frame her question, and Andreas came to her aid.

'You wondered if I intended, from the first, to make an annulment impossible?' She nodded and he went on, 'The idea did come early, but as I said, that was not the way I wanted it to be. I hoped you would come to me willingly. However, after those threats I did decide to put an end to those ideas of a break-up of our marriage.' He looked stern all at once and her lips trembled. Her husband was quick to notice, and to understand. 'You're tired, my love. It's a long rest for you now.' Putting her arm under the covers, he then pulled them up to her chin. 'Will you sleep, or must I give you something?'

'I'll sleep,' she returned happily and, after examining his face, 'You, darling, have you slept at all since last night? It was only last night it happened?'

'Last night? We wouldn't have brought you down this morning if it had happened only last night.' She had been unconscious for twenty-four hours, he went on to tell her, and after that she had been under drugs. 'I didn't really want to bring you down yet, but the weather forecast helped me decide. More heavy falls of snow are expected on Troodos and the road could be impassable for weeks.'

'You've had a long, anxious time,' she whispered huskily after dwelling for a moment on his words. 'I'll – I'll m-make it up to you, Andreas.'

'You already have – by loving me.' His deep voice

was oddly humble, and edged with gratitude. 'Bless you, darling.' He bent and kissed her, almost reverently. And when he straightened up she asked,

'When will I be out of bed?'

'Very soon. We'll have a wonderful Christmas together.'

'What's Cos like at this time?'

'You're not doing any travelling, my sweet.'

'Perhaps January?' She peeped up at him from under her lashes. 'After all, you did say it would be a wonderful place for a honeymoon.'

'There'll be no honeymoon until your doctor allows it.'

She swallowed hard. How could she ever have been so convinced that his only interest in her was desire?

Spring had come to the lovely island of Cos when they stood together on the heights of the Asclepion. Shani's cheeks were flushed with health, her hair windswept, her eyes sparkling. From all around came the scent of flowers; graceful cypresses swayed in the breeze, and the sun shone down from a cloudless Aegean sky.

Adoring eyes were lifted to her husband's face. Smiling, he took her hand and raised it to his lips.